Art in Focus

STUDY GUIDES

Rosalie J. Kotwas

Macmillan/McGraw-Hill

New York, New York   Columbus, Ohio   Mission Hills, California   Peoria, Illinois

Send all inquiries to:
GLENCOE DIVISION
Macmillan/McGraw-Hill
936 Eastwind Drive
Westerville, OH 43081-3374

ISBN 0-02-662321-8

Printed in the United States of America.

1 2 3 4 5 6 7 8 MAL 99 98 97 96 95 94 93

TABLE OF CONTENTS

TABLE OF CONTENTS

TABLE OF CONTENTS

TABLE OF CONTENTS

STUDY GUIDE 1

Name ______________________ Date ____________ Class Period ______

Directions This section explores the questions "What is Art?" and "What Is an Artist?" As you read Section 1, complete the following.

1. List the four steps of art criticism and describe what is done at each step.

   (a) ______________________________

   (b) ______________________________

   (c) ______________________________

   (d) ______________________________

2. Art history utilizes the same four steps to gather information, however, the four steps mean something different. List the four steps of art history and describe what is done at each step.

   (a) ______________________________

   (b) ______________________________

   (c) ______________________________

   (d) ______________________________

3. How does the art-history approach complete your study of a work of art?

   ____

4. A scholar who specializes in the study of the nature of beauty and art is called a(n) ______________.

5. Aestheticians who favor the realistic representation of subject matter are called ______________.

Name ______________________ Date ____________ Class Period ______

6. An aesthetic view held by ______________________ places importance on how well artists design their works.

7. ______________________ hold the aesthetic view that places the most importance on the vivid communication of ideas, feelings, and moods.

8. An individual who sponsors and supports activities in the arts is called a(n) ______________________ ______________________ .

9. Chairs, dishes, and clothing can be designed to be visually pleasing as well as functionally ______________________ .

10. Paintings and sculpture fall into the ______________________ ______________________ category.

STUDY GUIDE 2

Name ______________________ Date ______________ Class Period ________

Directions There are many career opportunities in the art field. As you read Section 2 and explore the career possibilities, complete the following.

1. The type of artist who purchases artworks, develops a collection, and understands law and taxation is called a(n) ______________________ .

2. An artist who combines visual images with news is called a(n) ______________________ .

3. The type of artist who presents newspaper, magazine, and television information that might show a product as an efficient tool is called a(n) ______________________ .

4. The type of artist who selects typefaces, lettering, and creates book-page layouts for publishers is called a(n) ______________________ .

5. The type of artist who uses a computer to create, alter, and store images is called a(n) ______________________ .

6. A(n) ______________________ assumes administrative responsibilities in public and private museums, libraries, theaters, concert halls, and art centers.

7. An artist who uses fabrics of different colors, textures, and weights to create garments is called a(n) ______________________ .

8. ______________________ are artists who design residences, office buildings, and museums.

9. Four materials used by landscape architects include ______________________ , ______________________ , ______________________ , and ______________________ .

10. What educational credentials are required of an art teacher? ______________________

11. What are the clues that help archaeologists determine how ancient people lived?

    ____

12. Explain the role of the museum curator. ______________________

13. List three things you can do if you have a commitment to becoming an artist.

    (a) ______________________

    (b) ______________________

    (c) ______________________

STUDY GUIDE 3

Name ______________________ Date ____________ Class Period ______

Directions Artists use the elements and principles of art to create unity in works of art. As you read Section 1, complete the following.

1. List the seven elements of art. ______________________

2. List the eight principles of art. ______________________

3. What is meant by an artist's style? ______________________

4. Using the description of an object on page 27 as a model, select and describe an object in terms of the following art elements:
   a. color ______________________
   b. value ______________________
   c. line ______________________
   d. texture ______________________
   e. shape ______________________
   f. form ______________________
   g. space ______________________

5. Name the three qualities of color. ______________________

6. Explain the difference between the intensity and the value of a hue. ______________________

7. Use an ordinary pencil to create a value scale. In the boxes below, make six different kinds of grays starting with the lightest gray and progressing to the darkest gray.

Name _______________ Date _______________ Class Period _______________

8. Fill out the color wheel below by writing the names of the primary, secondary, and intermediate (or tertiary) colors in the appropriate sequence.

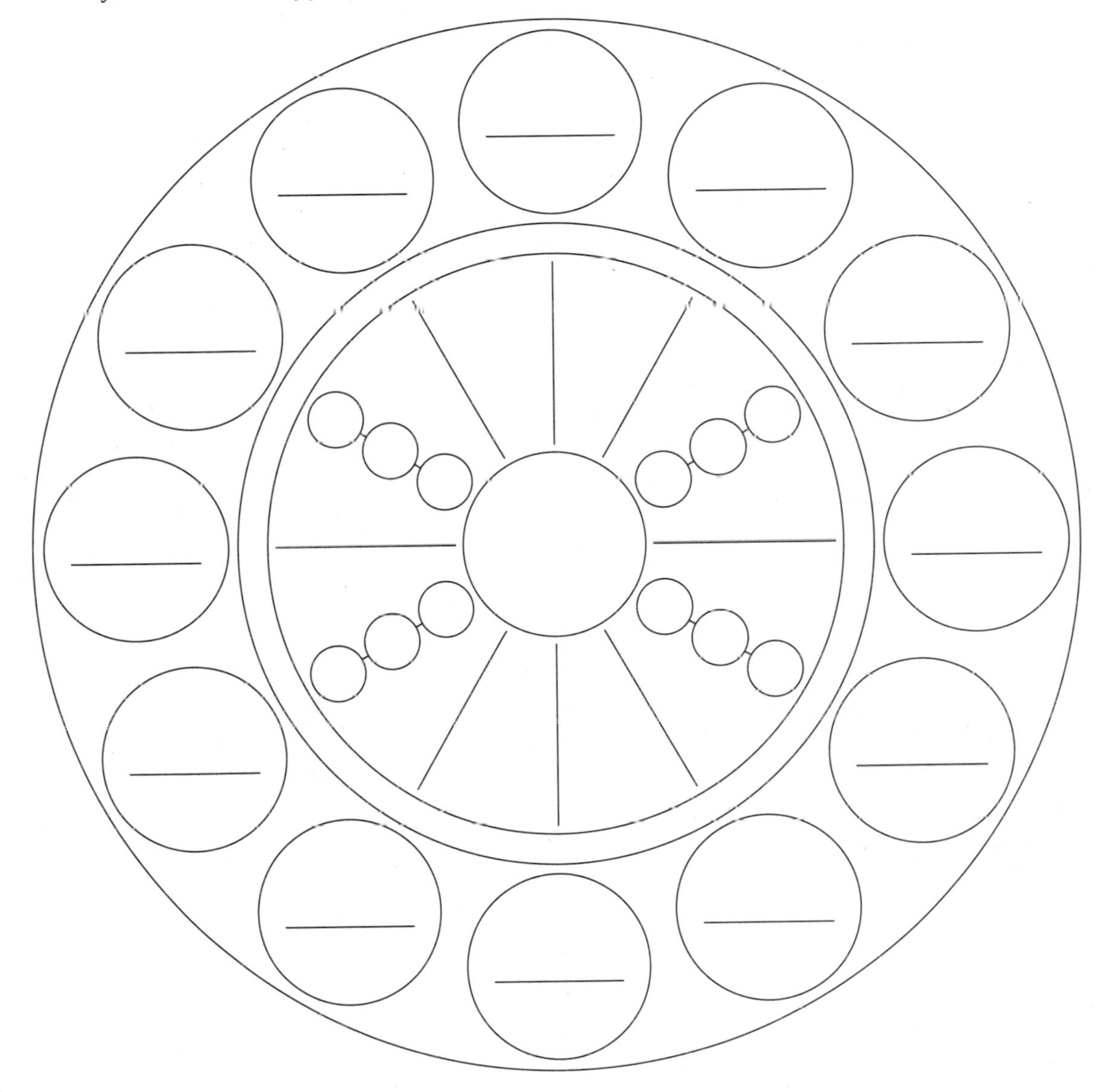

9. What types of artworks use value (apart from color)? _______________

____

10. Explain how changes in value can affect our perception of forms. _______________

____

____

STUDY GUIDE 4

Name ______ Date ______ Class Period ______

Directions Artists combine several different elements including line, texture, shape, form, and space to create works of art. As you read Section 2, complete the following.

1. What types of effects are created by using the following types of lines?
   a. Vertical line ______
   b. Horizontal line ______
   c. Diagonal line ______
   d. Axis line ______
   e. Contour line ______
2. Describe how the following artists created texture in their works.
   a. Gerard Ter Borch (Figure 2.11, page 35)
   ______
   b. José de Creeft (Figure 2.12, page 36)
   ______
3. What visual elements can be used to set off shape? ______
4. Explain the difference between a shape and a form. ______
5. Describe three ways an artist can create the illusion of depth, or of three dimensions, in a two-dimensional work of art.
   a. ______
   b. ______
   c. ______
6. Explain what is meant by the statement: ". . . space is an element that can be described as being either three-dimensional or two-dimensional."
   ______

STUDY GUIDE 5

Name ______________________ Date ____________ Class Period ______

Directions The principles of art are used to organize the elements of art. As you read Section 3, complete the following.

1. Balance refers to a way of combining the elements to add a sense of ______________________ to a work of art.

2. ______________________ balance means formal balance, while ______________________ balance is more informal.

3. ______________________, or contrast, is a way of combining elements to stress the differences between those elements.

4. ______________________ refers to a way of combining similar elements in an artwork to accent their similarities.

5. The principle of art, ______________________, is a way of combining elements to create intricate and complicated relationships.

6. Gradation is achieved by using a series of ______________________ in particular art elements.

7. ______________________ is a principle of art used to produce the look of action or motion and to guide the viewer's eye through the work of art.

8. Repeated patterns are one way of creating a sense of ______________________ in a work of art.

9. ______________________ refers to the relationship of certain elements to the whole and to each other.

10. The painting *Nude Descending a Staircase #2* by Marcel Duchamp (Figure 2.22, page 45) is a good example of what principle? ______________________

11. *Five O'Clock Tea,* by Mary Cassatt (Figure 2.16, page 41) achieves ______________________ by using smaller dark shapes and larger white shapes.

12. What is the purpose of the Design Chart?

____

____

____

STUDY GUIDE 6

Name ______________________ Date ____________ Class Period ________

Directions Two-dimensional works of art, such as drawings and paintings, are created using a variety of media and tools. As you read Section 1, complete the following.

1. Identify five types of dry media. ______________________

____

____

2. Define wet media and give two examples. ______________________

____

____

3. Explain how earlier artists used drawings. ______________________

____

4. What two ways do contemporary artists use drawings? ______________________

____

5. What are the advantages of artists maintaining sketchbooks? ______________________

____

6. Identify the type of art subject that is used in the artworks listed below.

portrait	landscape	dreams/imaginary
animals	historical	everyday surrounding
still life	religious	

a. Élisabeth Vigée-Lebrun. *Portrait of a Lady.* ______________________

b. John Frederick Peto. *The Old Violin.* ______________________

c. John Trumbull. *The Declaration of Independence.* ______________________

d. Jacob van Ruisdael. *Forest Scene.* ______________________

e. Henri Rousseau. *The Sleeping Gypsy.* ______________________

f. Rosa Bonheur. *Plowing in Nivernais.* ______________________

g. Guercino. *Saint Jerome and the Angel.* ______________________

STUDY GUIDE 7

Name ______________________ Date __________ Class Period ______

Directions Artists use the media and processes of printmaking and photography to create two-dimensional artworks. As you read Section 2, complete the following.

1. What artists are given credit for inventing printmaking?

 ____

2. What contribution did Johannes Gutenberg make to the printmaking process?

 ____

3. The four basic printmaking methods are ______________,

 ______________, ______________, and ______________.

4. In ______________ printing the image to be printed is raised from the background.

5. The meaning of the word ______________ is "to cut into."

6. What type of printmaking process uses a copper or zinc plate covered with a mixture of beeswax, asphalt, and resin known as ground?

 ____

7. ______________ is a printmaking method in which the image to be printed is drawn on limestone, zinc, or aluminum with a special greasy crayon.

8. A screen print that has been handmade by an artist is called a ______________.

9. What decisions must the serious photographer make before taking a photograph?

 ____

 ____

 ____

10. Name four artists who have created works of art in the twentieth century using the medium of photography.

 ____

 ____

 ____

STUDY GUIDE 8

Name ______________________ Date ____________ Class Period ______

Directions Sculptures are three-dimensional works of art. As you read Section 1, complete the following.

1. Explain how sculpture as an art form differs from painting.

2. What are the two types of relief sculptures and how do they differ?

3. What is "sculpture in the round"?

4. Name four types of materials a sculptor might use.

5. Compare Constantin Brancusi's sculptural pieces as shown in Figure 4.8 and Figure 4.9 on page 82. What similarities and differences do you notice?

6. Find another example of a bas-relief sculpture by looking in other chapters of *Art in Focus.* Write the title, figure number, and medium of the one you selected.

7. What aesthetic theory of art is most closely related to Duane Hanson's *Janitor,* Figure 4.1 on page 78?

STUDY GUIDE 9

Name ____________________ Date __________ Class Period ______

Directions Different processes and techniques are used to create sculptural pieces. As you read Section 2, complete the following.

1. Define the modeling process and explain what materials are used for this process. ____________________

2. Why is modeling referred to as an additive process? ____________________

3. What is the purpose of constructing an armature? ____________________

4. What is another name for the technique known as the "lost-wax" process? ____________________

5. Number the sentences below from 1 to 10 to describe the sequence of casting Giacometti's bronze portrait (Figure 4.16, page 88).

   ______ **a.** The wax-lined plaster sections were reassembled and filled with a solid core of fireproof material.

   ______ **b.** An outer fireproof mold, or investment, was made by placing the wax model, along with rods and fireproof core, upside down in a container.

   ______ **c.** The sculpture was taken from the kiln. The inner core and investment were removed. The pins, air vents, and conduits were cut off. The surface of the sculpture was cleaned.

   ______ **d.** A layer of melted wax was brushed onto the inside surface of each plaster section.

   ______ **e.** After the inner, fireproof core was dry, the plaster was removed, leaving the wax surface exposed. Metal pins pushed into the core through the wax held it in place.

   ______ **f.** Molten bronze was poured into the empty space between the inner core and the outer investment—replacing the wax area with metal.

   ______ **g.** A clay model of the figure was completed.

   ______ **h.** Plaster (or gelatine) was applied to the model in sections.

   ______ **i.** The investment was heated in a kiln and the melted wax allowed to run out, or be "lost." (The metal pins continue to hold the space between the core and the investment separate.)

   ______ **j.** Wax rods were attached to the exposed wax layer (around the core) to serve as air vents and conduits for the molten metal.

Name ______________________ Date ____________ Class Period ______

Directions As you read Section 1, complete the following.

1. Name the four steps of the art-history approach to learning about a work of art.

2. What is the difference between an artist's individual style and a group style?

3. Why was the group of artists with whom Renoir associated called the Impressionists?

4. What aspects of the group style, Impressionism, is apparent in the Renoir painting *A Girl with a Watering Can* on page 99?

5. What aspects of Renoir's individual style are evident in that same painting?

6. Which one aspect of Georges Rouault's individual style is the most evident in his painting *The Italian Woman* on page 100?

7. Give an example of how an art historian might use the information gathered by the steps of art criticism.

STUDY GUIDE 11

Name ______________________ Date ____________ Class Period ________

Part 1

Directions Art critics, like art historians, have their own methods of studying works of art. Review Section 2 and answer the following questions.

1. Write the steps or operations that accompany the questions asked in the art-criticism method of studying a work of art.

   a. What is the artistic worth or merit? ______________________

   ____

   b. What are the feelings, moods, or ideas communicated by the work? ______________________

   ____

   c. What is the subject matter? What are the elements of art in the work? ______________________

   ____

   d. How is it organized according to the principles of art? ______________________

   ____

2. What is the difference between internal and external cues in works of art? ______________________

   ____

   ____

3. What are three kinds of aesthetic qualities that can be observed in a work of art?

   ____

   ____

Part 2

Directions Classify the following activities into the steps of the art-criticism method in which they would occur by writing **D** (Description), **A** (Analysis), **I** (Interpretation), or **J** (Judgment) before each.

4. ______ Determining the meaning of a collage.
5. ______ Listing all of the objects that are shown in a painting.
6. ______ Locating the center of interest in a painting.
7. ______ Examining the formal balance achieved in a piece of gold jewelry.
8. ______ Trying to understand the meaning of symbols used in a drawing.
9. ______ Deciding if a work is successful.

Name ______________________ Date ____________ Class Period ______

Part 3

Directions Answer the following questions.

10. How is everyone "equal" when it comes to interpretation? ______________________

____

11. What is the advantage of using both the art-history and art-criticism methods of studying a work of art?

____

____

12. Do some works of art seem to require more of one approach than the other? If so, give examples from the chapter.

____

____

Part 4

Directions Examine the following works of art. Decide whether the artist used Imitationalism (**I**), Formalism (**F**), or Emotionalism (**E**) in the work. Fill in the blank with the appropriate letter. Briefly explain your answer. Some works may be correctly interpreted more than one way. The first example has been completed.

13. __E__ Louis Guglielmi: *Terror in Brooklyn,* Figure 5.15, page 110. Why? *Because of the strong mood of fear and isolation that is expressed in the huddled figures in the enclosure and the empty, lonely streets around them.*

14. ______ Sandro Botticelli: *The Adoration of the Magi,* Figure 2.10, page 34. Why?

____

15. ______ Luis Meléndez: *Still Life with Oranges, Jars, and Boxes of Sweets,* page 37. Why?

____

16. ______ Bridget Riley: *Entice 2,* page 30. Why?

____

17. ______ Piet Mondrian: *Diamond Painting in Red, Yellow, Blue,* page 111. Why?

____

STUDY GUIDE 12

Name ______________________ Date ____________ Class Period ______

Directions Scan the entire chapter and notice the many charts that have been provided to help you learn more about works of art. Study the painting *A View of Salisbury Cathedral* by John Constable on page 114. Then use the chart on page 116 to help you learn more about this painting and make a personal judgment about it. In the blank chart below, fill in specific information for the general categories that are given.

For example, beside Art Criticism, under Description, you will put such information as "Large cathedral; lines of trees close by and farther off; cloudy sky; small figures, animals," and so on. "Dark colors and shadows for near trees. Bright, lighter colors for cathedral and sky," and so on. Follow that procedure for the entire chart.

	Description	Analysis	Interpretation	Judgment
Art Criticism				
Art History				

STUDY GUIDE 13

Name ______________________ Date ______________ Class Period ______

Directions Humanity's earliest achievements can be seen in the artworks created during prehistoric times. As you complete Section 1, answer the following.

1. Prehistoric art has been found in many parts around the world including the caves in ______________________, Spain.
2. How would you describe the animal shown in Figure 6.2, page 127?

   ____

   ____

3. Describe how the following elements of art have been used in Figure 6.2.
   - **a.** Hues ______________________________
   - **b.** Values ______________________________
   - **c.** Lines ______________________________
   - **d.** Forms ______________________________
   - **e.** Texture ______________________________
4. How can the Design Chart help you analyze Figure 6.2? ______________________

   ____

5. What is your interpretation of Figure 6.2? ______________________

   ____

   ____

6. Based on the steps of art criticism, would you judge Figure 6.2 as being a successful work of art? Why or why not?

   ____

   ____

STUDY GUIDE 14

Name ______________________ Date ____________ Class Period ______

Directions Art-history operations can be used to judge works of art including prehistoric art. As you read Section 2, complete the following.

1. Some historians and archaeologists believe that early civilizations began around ________ years ago.
2. How does radiocarbon-dating determine the dates of once-living objects? ______________________
3. The Old Stone Age, or the Paleolithic period, is the historical period believed to have lasted from ______________ until about ______________.
4. How and when were the caves at Lascaux found? ______________________
5. Explain what makes the animals in the prehistoric cave paintings seem so lifelike. ______________
6. Describe post-and-lintel construction. ______________________
7. How did the cave artists make use of the forms of the cave walls to increase the reality of their painted animals?
8. Large monuments created from huge stone slabs that lie scattered across Europe, India, Asia, and even America are called ______________.
9. What architectural methods of prehistoric peoples are evident at Stonehenge in England?

STUDY GUIDE 15

Name ______________________ Date ____________ Class Period ______

Directions Along the Nile River a once-powerful, ancient civilization began leaving behind impressive monuments and tombs. As you read Section 1, complete the following questions.

1. The Nile River Valley was first settled by ______________________ about 5000 B.C., probably in pursuit of the animals they depended on for food.
2. The Nile River valley was an ideal place for a civilization to flourish because the river flooded each spring, bringing with it ______________________ ______________________ from the interior of Africa, making possible the successful cultivation of crops.
3. A powerful pharaoh named Menes established the first of Egypt's thirty-one dynasties in about 3100 B.C., establishing his capital in the city of ______________________ .
4. Approximately how long did the Old Kingdom, one of three important periods in ancient Egypt, last? ______________________
5. The Middle Kingdom lasted from 2050 until 1800 B.C., a time of ______________________ and ______________________ and prosperity in Egypt.
6. The most brilliant period in ancient Egyptian history was the ______________________ ______________________ . This period began in 1570 B.C. and lasted until 332 B.C.
7. One of the great warriors of the New Kingdom was ______________________ , who has been called the Napoleon of Egypt.
8. One of the last pharaohs, Ikhnaton, also called Amenhotep IV, broke with the traditional religious beliefs and established a religion that worshiped what he called ______________________ .
9. The pyramids were built during which Kingdom? ______________________
10. What was the purpose of the dead-end passages and false burial chambers in the Egyptian tombs?
    ____
    ____
11. Early burial tombs eventually evolved into the great pyramids. Make a rough sketch in the space below to show this evolution.

Mastaba	Step Pyramid	Pyramid

STUDY GUIDE 16

Name ______________________ Date ____________ Class Period ______

Directions Sculptures and paintings from ancient Egyptian civilizations have survived over the centuries. As you read Section 2, complete the following.

1. The translation of an Egyptian word for sculptor is "He who keeps alive." Explain this meaning.

____

____

2. Study the sculpture of Khafre as shown in Figure 7.7, page 149. How has the sculptor treated the face differently than the body?

____

____

3. Whose head is carved as the head of the Sphinx? Why is his head affixed to the body of a lion in this sculpture?

____

____

4. How does the facial expression on the *Fragment of Head of King Sesostris III* (Figure 7.9, page 150) reflect the political situation of the Middle Kingdom?

____

____

5. What effect did the prosperity of the New Kingdom have on the arts?

____

6. What do the portraits of Nakht and his wife shown in Figure 7.14 on page 154 tell about their position and rank?

____

7. Egyptian ______________________ was an early form of picture writing used to represent objects and communicate information.

STUDY GUIDE 17

Name ______________________ Date ____________ Class Period ________

Directions This section describes where and how early civilizations of Greece developed and also highlights Greek contributions to the arts. As you read Section 1, answer the following questions.

1. The earliest inhabitants of Greece are thought to have settled there around 2000 B.C., after which they were conquered by two invaders. Who were these invaders?

2. What factors kept the early Greek city-states from uniting to form a nation?

3. Explain why the Delian League was formed and how it operated.

4. Who was Pericles?

5. What factor, besides the Peloponnesian War, finally brought an end to the Athenian government of Pericles?

6. What was the Acropolis?

7. Why was Pericles's building of the Parthenon so bitterly resented by the other members of the Delian League?

Name ______________________ Date ____________ Class Period ________

8. Use the following terms to label the parts of a Greek temple in the diagram below: *capital, lintel, column, pediment, stylobate,* and *frieze.*

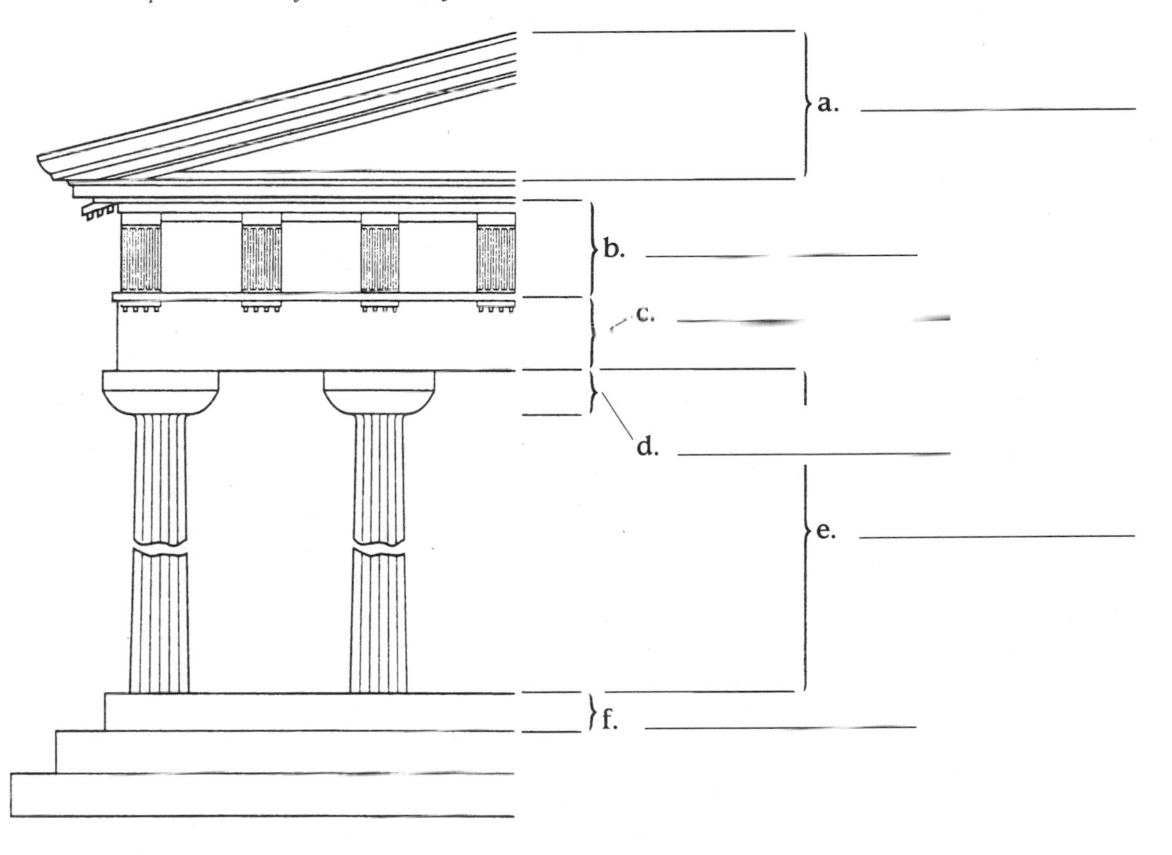

9. How was color used in the design of the Parthenon? ______________________

____

10. In addition to the Parthenon, what other kinds of Greek structures were built on the Acropolis?

____

____

11. Make a sketch of the capital of a **Doric** column, and briefly describe the capital and column.

____

____

____

Name ______________________ Date ____________ Class Period ________

12. Make a sketch of the capital of an **Ionic** column, and briefly describe the capital and column.

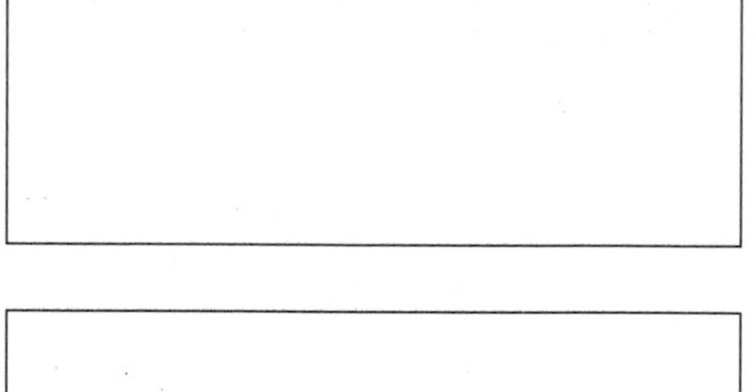

____

____

____

13. Make a sketch of the capital of a **Corinthian** column, and briefly describe the capital and column.

____

____

____

14. Describe the funeral vases painted in the Geometric Period.

____

15. How did the vase designs change after the Geometric Period?

____

STUDY GUIDE 18

Name ______________________ Date ____________ Class Period ______

Directions Many of the works of the ancient Greeks are considered classics of Western civilization. As you read Section 2, fill in the spaces from the word list below.

Apollo	early	Myron	clothed
cylinder	movement	athlete	Korai
Kouroi	arms	feet	texture
Archaic	Egyptian	spaces	

The time from 600 to 480 B.C. was called the **(1.)** ______________ period. Sculpture during this period resembled the statues of the **(2.)** ______________ sculptors, because of their unlifelike appearance and stiff, unnatural postures. The male statues, called **(3.)** ______________, were unclothed, standing, strong-looking figures. The illustration on page 174 may either have represented the sun god **(4.)** ______________ or an **(5.)** ______________. The pose is unnatural because of the placement of the **(6.)** ______________. This example differs from the Egyptian style in that there are **(7.)** ______________ cut out between the legs and between the **(8.)** ______________ and ______________. The female figures, of which Figure 8.17 on page 175 is an example, were called **(9.)** ______________. They were **(10.)** ______________ however; and the example on page 175 has no cut-out spaces. The lines on her garments are meant to suggest contrasting **(11.)** ______________ on her cloak and gown. Her stiff pose is not very lifelike; it is like a large stone **(12.)** ______________. The male figure showed some **(13.)** ______________ in the placement of the feet, but the female figure does not. The **(14.)** ______________ sculptors showed little of the skill of later artists such as **(15.)** ______________, the sculptor of *Discobolus* on page 176.

16. Contrast the two statues, *Kouros* (Figure 8.16, page 174) and *Discobolus* (Figure 8.18, page 176), by describing these aspects:

a. Posture ______________________________

____

b. Movement ______________________________

____

c. Texture ______________________________

____

d. Realism of anatomy ______________________________

____

Name ______________________ Date ____________ Class Period ______

17. Describe the statue of Athena by Phidias that stood outside on the western edge of the Acropolis.

18. Describe the statue of Athena that was inside the Parthenon.

19. If you were a citizen of Athens, Greece, where might you have seen the processional relief pictured in Figure 8.21 on page 179?

20. How does Polyclitus create the feeling of athletic strength and confidence in his sculpture *Doryphorus (Spear Bearer)* (Figure 8.23, page 180)?

21. The three statues mentioned below share the characteristic *contrapposto* pose. Describe the *contrapposto* position of each statue.

Doryphorus ____________________

The Dying Gaul ____________________

Seated Boxer ____________________

STUDY GUIDE 19

Name ______________________ Date ______________ Class Period ______

Directions Although the Roman Empire stretched from Britain to Mesopotamia, much of its art was copied from the Greeks. As you read Section 1, answer the following questions.

1. Who were the Etruscans? ______________________

2. Why did the Romans often commission portrait heads instead of sculptures of the entire body?

3. Which theory of art (imitationalism, formalism, emotionalism) did the Romans value most in their portrait sculptures? Explain why you think so.

4. Describe how the murals in Roman homes sometimes extended into a world beyond the walls.

5. What was discovered about Roman paintings from the excavations of Pompeii?

6. Compare the Roman use of columns with the way the Greeks used them.

7. Although the Temple of Fortuna Primigenia (Figure 9.9, page 194) looks at first glance very much like a Greek building, it incorporates a feature borrowed from the Etruscan style. What is that feature?

8. How was the arch an improvement over the post-and-lintel system favored by the Greeks?

9. What two building innovations did the Roman legions introduce wherever they went?

10. Describe what some believe to be the most important Roman construction in Spain.

STUDY GUIDE 20

Name ______________________ Date ____________ Class Period ________

Directions Throughout the Roman Empire, Roman buildings and monuments were numerous and impressive. As you read Section 2, answer the following questions.

1. How were the ancient Roman baths like shopping centers today? ______________________

____

2. Describe how different types of columns were used in the building of the Colosseum.

____

____

3. What was the original purpose of the Pantheon? ______________________

____

4. What did each of the three zones of the interior of the Pantheon represent?

____

____

5. How is the dome's exterior appearance different from its interior appearance?

____

____

6. Why are basilicas important in the history of architecture? ______________________

____

7. Describe how the triumphal arches were used in Roman times. ______________________

____

8. How did the design of the arches relate to their function? ______________________

____

9. How did the Arch of Bara in Spain (Figure 9.27, page 205) differ from most other Roman triumphal arches?

____

____

STUDY GUIDE 21

Name ______________________ Date ____________ Class Period ______

Directions The religions of Hinduism and Buddhism influenced the architecture and sculpture of the art of India. As you read Section 1, answer the following questions.

1. What were some of the developments of the Harappans, or people of the Indus Valley?

2. Describe how the religion of Hinduism began.

3. List the three main Hindu gods and explain what three primary processes in the universe they represent.

   a.

   b.

   c.

4. Explain the meaning of reincarnation.

5. Who founded the religion of Buddhism? When?

6. What types of architecture were built after Siddhartha Gautama's death that were influenced by the religious beliefs of Buddhism?

7. Why did the carvings and sculptures at the Great Stupa at Sanchi (Figure 10.6, page 216) not show the figure of Buddha?

8. What are some characteristics of Buddhist sculptures and carvings in the Gupta era (A.D. 320 to A.D. 600) that became models for future sculpture?

Name ______________________ Date ____________ Class Period ______

9. How did the Hindu temples differ in purpose from the Buddhist architecture?

____

____

____

10. Describe the symbolism associated with the bronze sculpture of *Shiva, the Dancing Lord* (Figure 10.11, page 220).

____

____

11. Why is it important to understand the religious beliefs of Buddhism and Hinduism in relation to the art of not only India, but China and Japan as well?

____

____

____

STUDY GUIDE 22

Name ______________________ Date ____________ Class Period ______

Directions Chinese civilization can lay claim as being the oldest continuous culture in the world. As you read Section 2, answer the following questions.

1. What two art forms were developed during the very early Chinese dynasties? ______________________

2. Explain how the art of China was affected by the arrival of Buddhism. ______________________

3. What is a Bodhisattva? ______________________

4. How was the human figure in Chinese sculpture different from a classical Greek sculpture? ______________________

5. What type of painting became the major subject of Chinese art during the eleventh century? ______________________

6. Describe two types of early scrolls. Tell how they were used. ______________________

7. What two kinds of sculpture were produced during the T'ang dynasty? ______________________

8. What do the inscriptions and seals placed on Chinese paintings represent? ______________________

9. What art form was perfected during the Sung period? ______________________

10. How does the changing vanishing point influence the way a viewer interprets Chinese art? ______________________

11. What is regarded as the most significant accomplishment in the art of the Ming dynasty? ______________________

STUDY GUIDE 23

Name ____________________ Date __________ Class Period ______

Directions After the ninth century the style of Japanese art began to develop its own style. As you read Section 3, complete the following questions.

1. Explain how Buddhism was introduced to Japan.

2. Why have the Japanese developed the art of constructing wooden buildings and not the stone structures favored by many other cultures?

3. Why is the temple at Horyuji so important to the history of Japanese art?

4. What was the purpose of the pagodas built at the Horyuji Temple?

5. What period is regarded as the golden age of Japanese art?

6. What is Yamato-e and why is it important to Japanese art history?

7. Why was there such a demand for art during the Edo period and what art form developed as a result of this demand?

8. What does Ukiyo-e mean and what art form depicted it?

9. What was an advantage of woodblock printing over other art forms?

10. What was Harunobu's innovative achievement?

STUDY GUIDE 24

Name ______________________ Date ____________ Class Period ______

Directions Native Americans settled in North America more than twenty thousand years ago. As you read Section 1, complete the following questions.

1. What are the subjects of most of the art created by Inuit artists? ______________________

2. Describe the Inuit engravings in terms of the subjects portrayed, size, and materials used.

3. How were the customs of the Hamatsa tribe of the Northwest Coast region related to their creation of masks and costumes?

4. How did the annual initiation rituals of the Hamatsa society differ from a potlatch?

5. Describe a totem pole and tell what function it served among the Native Americans of the Northwest Coast.

6. What kind of dwellings are characteristic of the Pueblo people? What materials did they use and how were their buildings arranged?

7. How did the art of Navajo weaving change from the beginning of the eighteenth century through the nineteenth century?

8. What artistic skills were evident among the different tribes of the Great Plains?

Name ______________________________ Date ______________ Class Period ________

9. What qualities did the Adena artists portray in their small 8-inch (20-cm) high figures carved of pipestone?

____

____

10. What did the False Face of the Iroquois masks represent? ____________________

____

11. How did the Iroquois masks in the Woodlands region compare with the Hamatsa masks of the Northwest region?

____

____

STUDY GUIDE 25

Name ______________________ Date ____________ Class Period ______

Directions Pre-Columbian is used when referring to the various cultures and civilizations found throughout North and South America before 1492. As you read Section 2, answer the following questions.

1. What is conveyed on the face of the Olmec jadeite mask of an Olmec ruler that is also on the gigantic heads carved in volcanic rock?

2. What religious beliefs explain the Mayan rituals and ceremonies of drawing blood and sacrificing captives of war?

3. How were the Mayan central plazas decorated?

4. What time period spans the Mayan culture? How did it end?

5. If you were to visit Tenochtitlan during the rule of the Aztecs, what kind of architecture and city would you most likely see?

6. What warlike behavior contrasted the Aztecs' cleanly scrubbed palaces and streets?

7. How was the human figure portrayed in Aztec paintings?

8. How did a legend of the Aztecs contribute to the end of their empire?

9. What system of transportation and communication did the Incas develop?

STUDY GUIDE 26

Name ______________________ Date __________ Class Period ______

Directions As you read Section 1, examine the African metal artworks and complete the following questions.

1. What was the great artistic accomplishment of the Ife and Benin artists? ______________________

2. Why was the Western art world so astonished by a shipment of the artworks to England in 1897? ______________________

3. What was the original purpose of the Benin high-relief sculptures? ______________________

4. Examine the reproduction of a metal casting on page 268. Describe the details that demonstrate the skill and artistic ability of the African sculptors. ______________________

5. What metals were used in African artworks? ______________________

6. What kinds of items were made by the Akan goldsmiths? ______________________

7. What did gold symbolize for the Akan people? Why were the items made from gold intended for kings? ______________________

8. Explain how metal was used in Ethiopian Christianity from the fifteenth century to the nineteenth. ______________________

STUDY GUIDE 27

Name ______________________ Date ____________ Class Period ________

Directions As you read Section 2, examine African works in wood and complete the following.

1. What were the main kinds of carved-wood objects that the Africans made? ____________________

2. How did the climate of Africa affect the quality of mask production? ____________________

3. What four features are common to all African wooden figure sculptures, regardless of where they were produced?

4. Name the three types of figure carvings discussed in Section 2 of Chapter 12. Then list the title of a work that is an example of each type.

	Type of Figure Carving	Work of Art
a.		
b.		
c.		

5. Complete the chart below for the three examples on pages 276 and 278. Briefly describe the dominant art element used by the artist, the principal materials used, and the original purpose of the object.

		Dominant Art Element(s)	Materials	Purpose
a.	Nimba Headdress (Figure 12.15)			
b.	Songye Face Mask (Figure 12.17)			
c.	Bundu Society Mask (Figure 12.18)			

STUDY GUIDE 28

Name ______________________ Date ____________ Class Period ______

Directions Christianity spread rapidly across the Roman Empire influencing the art and architecture of the times. As you read Section 1, answer the following questions.

1. For what two purposes were the catacombs created? ______________________

2. How did the Christian outlook on life differ from that of Romans? ______________________

3. How were these Christian attitudes reflected in their paintings? Use Figure 13.2, page 287 as your example.

4. Why were the details of the life of Christ so often the subject for early Christian art?

5. What did the following symbols mean to early Christians?
   a. shepherd ______________________
   b. goldfinch ______________________
   c. peacock ______________________
   d. dog ______________________
   e. ivy ______________________

6. How did the exterior and interior of early Christian churches differ? ______________________

7. What did the mosaics in the early Christian churches illustrate? ______________________

8. Describe two details in the mosaic Figures 13.12 and 13.13, page 294 that demonstrate the formalist theory of art.

Name ______________________ Date ____________ Class Period ________

9. What three cultures influenced Byzantine art? ______________________

10. How is the Byzantine art related to the Christian religion? ______________________

11. In what three ways was the Byzantine dome an improvement over the Roman dome? ______________________

12. Why were mosaics rather than paintings used to decorate the walls of the churches? ______________________

STUDY GUIDE 29

Name ______________________________ Date ______________ Class Period ______

Directions Islam as a major religion appeared in the Middle East in the seventh century. As you read Section 2, answer the following questions.

1. What is the Koran? ______________________________

2. How does the art of the interior of an Islamic mosque differ from that of a Christian church? Explain why.

3. In what ways was the mosque of Cordoba (Mesquita) similar to the mosque in Granada (the Alhambra)?

4. Explain why Islamic artists illustrated everyday scenes rather than other subjects.

5. What is characteristic of Islamic books, as well as the furnishings of palaces and mosques in Spain?

6. When and where did the art of Islamic book illustration reach its peak?

7. What are some of the elements of art found in the sixteenth-century miniature illustration by the artist Mussawir (Figure 13.29, page 305)?

STUDY GUIDE 30

Name ______________________ Date ____________ Class Period ______

Part 1

Directions The Church played a central role in the daily lives of medieval people. As you read Section 1, answer the following questions. You may use some words more than once.

Charlemagne	Early	Middle Ages	Aix-la-Chapelle
Medieval	Dark Ages	Gothic	
arts	Romanesque	Ravenna	

The period from A.D. 500 to 1500 in western Europe has been given three names by historians. It has been called the **(1.)** ______________, the **(2.)** ______________ period, and the **(3.)** ______________. One of these names, **(4.)** ______________, is misleading, because although it has been called a time of "blank pages" in history, it was actually a time of great accomplishment. Historians divide this period into three parts, the Early **(5.)** ______________, from the last half of the fifth century to the middle of the eleventh; the **(6.)** ______________, which lasted through the twelfth century, and the **(7.)** ______________ period, which overlapped and lasted until approximately the sixteenth century.

In the year 800, **(8.)** ______________ was crowned emperor of the Holy Roman Empire. He was to be important in many aspects of history, including his encouragement of learning and the **(9.)** ______________. The capital of his empire was at **(10.)** ______________, where there is still a beautiful chapel, resembling the church at **(11.)** ______________ which he built in the late 700s.

Part 2

Directions Respond to the questions in the spaces provided.

12. What factors led to the feudal system of government?

____

13. Pretend you are either a serf, a vassal, or a lord, and explain how feudalism worked from your viewpoint. Circle the role you have chosen.

SERF VASSAL LORD

____

____

Name ______________________ Date ____________ Class Period ______

14. What two changes in the basic basilica style were made for the churches of the Middle Ages?

15. What symbolic design results from the addition of the transept?

16. What was the purpose of building monasteries?

17. Study the illustrations on pages 314-318. Does the "monastic life" seem to relate to the art and architecture of this period? If you think it does, explain how. If you think not, write your reasons why not.

18. What is the setting of the monastery of San Juan de la Peña?

19. What is an illuminated manuscript?

20. Look at the reproduction of *St. Matthew* on page 317. Describe how the artist used the art element of line in this painting.

STUDY GUIDE 31

Name ________________ Date ________ Class Period ______

Part 1

Directions The Romanesque period had been accepted throughout western Europe by the eleventh century. As you read Section 2, answer the following questions.

1. In what ways did the function of castles determine their design? Refer to at least three details of their structure.

____

____

2. Castles were symbols of authority and wealth during the Romanesque period. What cultural changes caused their ruin and decline?

____

____

3. Briefly describe the evolution of cities. What caused them to come into being?

____

____

4. What was the biggest problem of medieval cities? How did it affect the way buildings were constructed?

____

____

5. What kind of building did every medieval town have? What purposes did it serve?

____

____

6. Define *pilgrimage.* What kind of pilgrimages were made by Europeans in medieval times?

____

____

7. Describe three design modifications that enlarged the standard Roman church.

____

____

8. What was the greatest challenge to Romanesque church designers?

____

____

Name ______________________ Date ____________ Class Period ______

9. What church construction was borrowed from the Romans to solve this problem? Was it always successful?

____

____

10. Study the design and plan of San Sernin in Toulouse, France, Figures 14.16, 14.17, and 14.18 on pages 323-324. What are two characteristics of Romanesque architecture that you notice?

____

____

11. Study Figure 14.21 on page 325 and describe an example of how this Romanesque relief sculpture sacrificed realism for emotionalism.

____

____

STUDY GUIDE 32

Name ______________________ Date ____________ Class Period ______

Directions The Gothic style emerged around the middle of the twelfth century and lasted to the end of the fifteenth century. As you read about the Gothic style, complete the following questions.

1. Briefly describe how and why the feudal system came to an end. ______________________

2. Explain why the Gothic period is so named. ______________________

3. Why is "Gothic Cathedral" a misnomer? ______________________

4. Compare the Gothic and Romanesque designs by completing the following chart.

	Features	Romanesque Design	Gothic Design Innovation
a.	Wall supports		
b.	Arches		
c.	Decoration		
d.	Light		

5. Why were the supporting arches called "flying buttresses"? ______________________

6. What are two important advantages of the flying buttress construction? ______________________

7. What did stained-glass windows have in common with illuminated manuscripts? ______________________

8. Describe, in your own words, how stained glass was colored, and how stained-glass pictures were created.

____

9. How were Gothic churches and cathedrals financed? What was the reward for people of the community who made donations toward the building of the Gothic churches and cathedrals?

____

STUDY GUIDE 33

Name ______________________ Date ____________ Class Period ______

Directions During the Gothic period, the arts used to decorate the cathedrals prospered. As you read Section 2, complete the following.

1. How did Gothic sculpture differ from Romanesque? ______________________

2. What features indicate a growing concern for reality in the sculpture of the Burgos Cathedral (Figures 15.13a and 15.13b, page 345)?

3. Describe the expressive qualities of the Golden Virgin statue (Figure 15.15, page 346). ______________________

4. What are gargoyles? Why were they placed on the roof lines of Gothic buildings? ______________________

5. What is meant by the International style? ______________________

6. What are some of the artistic characteristics of the International style? ______________________

7. Select three aspects of the International style that you find interesting; then describe and explain your choices.

8. What is a "psalter"? How do the illustrations differ from a "book of hours"? ______________________

Name ____________________ Date ____________ Class Period ________

9. Fill in the missing information in the chart.

Title (Work of Art)	Artist	Location	Dates
a. (Figure 15.1) ______	The Limbourg Brothers		1413–16
b. *The Martyrdom of Thomas à Becket* (Figure 15.18)			Mid-13th Century

10. The chart above contains the material you would use as part of an art-history operation to study a particular work. Choose one of the two and make out the entire art-history chart below.

Art-History Operations			
Description	Analysis	Interpretation	Judgment

STUDY GUIDE 34

Name ______________________ Date ____________ Class Period ______

Part 1

Directions Examine the section on Italian church painting and answer the questions in the spaces provided.

1. Why wasn't the Gothic style popular in Italy? ______________________

2. Look carefully at Duccio's altarpiece painting (page 350) and describe two details that illustrate the Byzantine style.

3. In what way are Duccio's figures different from the usual Byzantine style? ______________________

4. What is a fresco painting? ______________________

5. Write the "recipe" and directions for creating a fresco. Include the ingredients and the step-by-step process, using information from your textbook.

6. Fresco paintings have a particular "look"—quite different from paintings that are made from other materials. Using your own words, describe the distinctive appearance of a fresco.

7. Describe a few of the ways Giotto depicts emotionalism in his fresco *Lamentation* (page 352).

Name ______________________ Date ____________ Class Period ______

Part 2

Directions Make a thorough study of Giotto's *Lamentation* on page 352. Complete the charts and write the evaluations as directed for each step. Refer to Chapters 2 and 5 if needed.

8. Complete the design chart for Giotto's *Lamentation*, checking those art elements and art principles that apply.

		Principles of Art						
		Balance	Emphasis	Harmony	Variety	Gradation	Movement/ Rhythm	Proportion
Elements of Art	Color: Hue							
	Intensity							
	Value							
	Value (Non-Color)							
	Line							
	Texture							
	Shape/Form							
	Space							

Directions Now that you have carefully examined the way the art elements and principles were used in *Lamentation*, decide which of the theories of art, as studied in Chapter 5, apply to this painting. Look at the chart on page 111 and complete the following.

9. Does *Lamentation* display the literal qualities you might call Imitationalism? Why or why not?

____

10. Does it display the visual qualities that would lead you to categorize it as Formalism? Why or why not?

____

____

11. Does it display the expressive qualities that would lead you to call it Emotionalism? Why or why not?

____

____

STUDY GUIDE 36

Name ______________________________ Date ______________ Class Period ________

Directions As you read Section 1 and learn about the beginnings of the Italian Renaissance, answer the following questions in the spaces provided.

1. Write a definition for the term *Renaissance.* ______________________________

2. While artists in the North were creating stained-glass windows and illuminated manuscripts, how were the Italian painters decorating their churches?

3. Where is the city of Florence and why was it important in the Renaissance? ______________________________

4. Give two examples of how the renewed interest in classical art affected the appearance of the artworks of the early Renaissance.

5. Explain the concept of "middle class." ______________________________

6. How did the emergence of the middle class change the art world? ______________________________

7. What factors contributed to Italy's becoming the center for the development of painting? ______________________________

8. What were two innovations in the paintings of Masaccio? ______________________________

9. What was Masaccio's preferred medium? ______________________________

Name ______________________ Date ____________ Class Period ______

10. Compare linear and aerial perspective. Tell how the illusion of depth is created with each method.

11. Who was Filippo Brunelleschi, and what did he discover?

12. How would using a mirror help Brunelleschi discover how to create linear perspective?

13. Why does Masaccio's *The Tribute Money* use both linear and aerial perspective?

14. Describe Fra Angelico's style of painting.

15. What details of Fra Angelico's *The Annunciation* (Figure 16.7, page 365) are typical of the early Renaissance?

16. What was Lorenzo Ghiberti's first great success?

17. Name an artist in addition to Ghiberti who entered the contest to decorate the Baptistry doors of the Cathedral of Florence.

18. Compare the two sets of doors Ghiberti and Brunelleschi created for the Baptistry of the Florence Cathedral.

19. What was Michelangelo's response when he saw the doors? What name was later given to the doors?

STUDY GUIDE 37

Name ______________________ Date ____________ Class Period ________

Directions As you examine Renaissance sculpture and architecture in Section 2, answer the questions in the spaces provided.

1. Which artists' innovations did Piero della Francesca pick up and carry forward? ____________

____

2. Write three observations about the formalism in Piero della Francesca's painting *The Baptism of Christ*.

a. ____

b. ____

c. ____

3. What was Piero della Francesca's greatest contribution to the development of painting?

____

4. Explain how Donatello made use of perspective in his sculptures. ____________

____

____

5. Compare Donatello's *St. George* with the classical Greek sculpture *Doryphorus (Spear Bearer)* by Polyclitus (page 180) by describing an important similarity, and one difference.

____

____

6. What happened to Filippo Brunelleschi after he lost the contest for the Baptistry doors?

____

7. How did Brunelleschi solve the design problems in building the dome for the Florence Cathedral?

____

____

8. Sketch a diagram of his dome design in the space below.

Name ______________________________ Date ______________ Class Period ________

9. What style did Brunelleschi use for his design of the Pazzi Chapel? ______________________________

____

____

10. Who were Sandro Botticelli's patrons? How did they influence his painting? ______________________

____

____

11. What aesthetic qualities are dominant in *The Adoration of the Magi* (see page 373)? ______________

____

____

12. Make a diagram of Botticelli's composition below. Use only geometric shapes to help you understand the importance of the design elements in Botticelli's work.

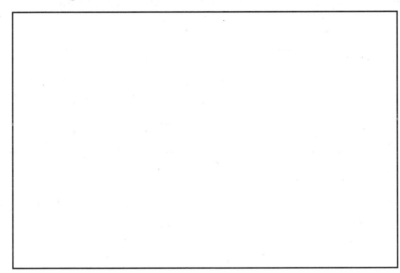

13. How does Botticelli's decision to place the Madonna and Child in the ruins of a classical building demonstrate the Renaissance philosophy?

____

____

14. In what way did the art patrons immortalize themselves? ______________________________

____

STUDY GUIDE 38

Name ______________________ Date ______________ Class Period ________

Directions Answer the questions in the spaces provided.

1. List five of Leonardo da Vinci's areas of knowledge.

   a. ______________________

   b. ______________________

   c. ______________________

   d. ______________________

   e. ______________________

2. How and why did Leonardo study anatomy? ______________________

3. What aspect of Leonardo's personality made it difficult for him to complete many of his artwork projects?

4. Like countless other Renaissance artists, Leonardo painted a version of *The Last Supper.* In what ways did Leonardo break with tradition in his interpretation?

5. The United States has only one painting by Leonardo. What is its name, and what museum would you have to visit in order to see it?

6. Study the work on page 376 carefully and choose three words to describe the emotional quality of the painting.

7. What famous Leonardo painting remains unfinished? ______________________

8. Why was it never finished? ______________________

Name ______________________ Date ____________ Class Period ______

9. Describe the sculpture called the *Pietà* by Michelangelo. ______________________

____

____

10. What is the error in proportion in the *Pietà*, and what might this disproportion mean when interpreting the expressive qualities of the statue?

____

____

11. Why did Michelangelo not finish the tomb for Pope Julius? ______________________

____

12. List three reasons Michelangelo was reluctant to paint the ceiling of the Sistine Chapel.

a. ______________________

b. ______________________

c. ______________________

13. Explain how Michelangelo organized the space in his painting on the Sistine Chapel ceiling.

____

____

14. Which theory of art can best be applied to Michelangelo's *The Creation of Adam* (page 378)?

____

15. How was Raphael's life different from that of Michelangelo? ______________________

____

16. What did Raphael learn from Leonardo? ______________________

____

____

17. What did Raphael learn from Michelangelo? ______________________

____

____

18. What were some of the attitudes during the Renaissance that made it difficult for women to become artists? Explain your answer.

____

____

STUDY GUIDE 39

Name ______________________ Date ____________ Class Period ________

Part 1

Directions As you explore the progress of painting during the fifteenth century in northern Europe, answer the following questions in the spaces provided.

1. What painting tradition had the greatest influence on the fifteenth-century northern European artists?

2. What two ideas or goals interested most of the northern European artists?

3. Explain the traditional method of using tempera paint.

4. What were the limitations of tempera paint, especially on fresco paintings?

5. What are the advantages of oil paint?

6. Who is credited with the invention of the technique of painting with oil paint?

7. Study the picture of the painting of *Giovanni Arnolfini and His Bride* on page 391 and identify three symbols that were used in paintings of that day. Briefly interpret their meanings.

8. What is the most striking aspect of the painting technique in *Giovanni Arnolfini and His Bride*?

9. What is the name of the twelve-part altarpiece Jan van Eyck painted? Briefly describe the central panel.

10. What theory of art is most obvious in the work of van Eyck?

Name ______________________ Date ____________ Class Period ______

Part 2

Directions Using the art-history and art-criticism charts, make a detailed study of van Eyck's *Giovanni Arnolfini and His Bride.*

11. Read the text and study the picture on page 391; then fill out the art-history chart.

Art-History Operations			
Description	Analysis	Interpretation	Judgment

12. Using what you have learned, what is your judgment about the painting *Giovanni Arnolfini and His Bride*? Tell whether you think it is an important work in the history of art and why.

____

____

13. Look carefully again at *Giovanni Arnolfini and His Bride* as you complete the art-criticism chart.

Art-Criticism Operations			
Description	Analysis	Interpretation	Judgment

14. Do you think *Giovanni Arnolfini and His Bride* is a successful painting? Why or why not?

____

____

STUDY GUIDE 40

Name ______________________ Date ____________ Class Period ________

Part 1

Directions Northern European fifteenth-century art gradually developed into a style that combined realism and emotionalism. As you read Section 2, answer the following questions.

1. What contributions did Rogier van der Weyden make to fifteenth-century northern painting?

____

____

2. What valuable tradition did van der Weyden preserve? ______________________

____

3. Look carefully at van der Weyden's *Descent from the Cross* on page 394 and van Eyck's *Adoration of the Lamb* on page 393 and identify two differences between the artists and their paintings.

____

____

4. Diagram the ten figures arranged around the cross in Rogier van der Weyden's *Descent from the Cross* in the space below. Use a single curved line for each figure.

Name ______________________ Date ______________ Class Period ________

5. How does the shape of the panel enhance the meaning of the painting? ______________________

____

____

6. What is the meaning of the two hands: the right hand of Christ and the left hand of Mary in the foreground of *Descent from the Cross*?

____

____

7. What two kinds of visual information does van der Weyden provide about the subject in *Portrait of a Lady* (page 395)? What are the clues?

____

____

8. What is unusual about the appearance of Hugo van der Goes's painting on page 397?

____

____

9. What characteristics in the work of Rogier van der Weyden and Jan van Eyck were combined and used by Hugo van der Goes?

____

____

10. Describe van der Goes's use of space in *The Adoration of the Shepherds.* ______________________

____

____

11. How was van der Goes's interpretation of the three shepherds revolutionary? ______________________

____

____

Name ______________________ Date ____________ Class Period ________

Part 2

Directions Review the three art theories—Imitationalism, Formalism, and Emotionalism—and respond to the questions about van der Goes's *The Adoration of the Shepherds.*

12. What are the literal qualities of *The Adoration of the Shepherds* that would make you agree or disagree that this painting represents Imitationalism?

____

____

13. What are the design qualities of *The Adoration of the Shepherds* that would make you agree or disagree that this painting represents Formalism?

____

____

14. What are the qualities of *The Adoration of the Shepherds* that would make you agree or disagree that this painting represents Emotionalism?

____

____

15. There are at least three traditional symbols in the painting *The Adoration of the Shepherds.* Name them and tell what they mean.

a. ____

b. ____

c. ____

STUDY GUIDE 41

Name ______________________ Date ______________ Class Period ________

Directions Venetian artists turned to their beautiful and unique island city as a source of inspiration. As you read Section 1, answer the following questions.

1. Tell how the art of Venice was influenced by Byzantine art. Compare that to the classical Greek and Roman influence on the Florentine artists.

2. What subject element did Giorgione bring out of the background and into the body of his paintings?

3. What was the visible result of Giorgione's use of oil paints? What new effect did he achieve?

4. What special details did Giorgione use to create the serene but mysterious mood in *The Concert* (page 406)?

5. In this text, Giorgione is considered the painter of *The Concert*; however, some scholars believe it was partially or entirely painted by Titian. Look at *The Concert*, and then study the two paintings by Titian (page 407). What significant differences do you observe between *The Concert* and the two paintings that are authentically Titian's?

6. How was Titian influenced by Giorgione?

7. Contrast the mood of *The Concert* with that of *The Entombment*. How have the artists created different moods?

8. What other master painter do you think influenced Titian? Explain why.

STUDY GUIDE 42

Name ______________________ Date ____________ Class Period ________

Directions As you examine art of the Mannerist period and read Section 2, answer the following questions.

1. In what setting did Mannerist art evolve? What was going on in the world during that time?

2. List three words that describe the mood and atmosphere of Mannerist art.

3. Which Mannerist artist painted *The Madonna with the Long Neck*?

4. Read the interpretation of *The Madonna with the Long Neck* on pages 410 and 411, and describe three details from the painting that contribute most to its mysterious mood.

5. Examine Tintoretto's *Presentation of the Virgin* on page 412, and give two reasons for classifying it as a Mannerist work of art.

6. What kind of paintings did the Church welcome to counter the Reformation?

7. Name two artists who influenced El Greco, and describe what he learned from them.

8. What is ironic about El Greco's painting *The Martyrdom of St. Maurice and the Theban Legion*?

9. Name and describe the painting that El Greco considered his greatest. Tell what it signified.

Name ______________________ Date ____________ Class Period ______

10. What are the probable identities of the only two figures in *The Burial of Count Orgaz* who are looking out at the viewer?

____

____

Part 2

Directions Study El Greco's *The Burial of Count Orgaz* further by using the art study operations you have learned.

11. Complete the art-history and art-criticism operations to further study *The Burial of Count Orgaz* by making notes in the chart below.

	Description	Analysis	Interpretation	Judgment
Art Criticism				
Art History				

12. Now that you have studied this painting, what is your opinion of *The Burial of Count Orgaz*?

____

____

STUDY GUIDE 43

Name ______________________ Date ____________ Class Period ________

Directions As you read about the conflicting artistic style that occurred during the fifteenth century, answer the following questions.

1. How do the two styles of Italian Renaissance art and Late Gothic art differ?

2. How are these differences reflected in the work of Grünewald and Dürer?

3. Compare the emotional impact of Grünewald's *The Small Crucifixion* on page 417 with Raphael's *The Alba Madonna* on page 381.

4. Which of these two paintings do you prefer, and why?

5. What event in Albrecht Dürer's life changed his attitude and style of art? How?

6. Study the engraving of *Knight, Death, and the Devil* by Dürer, and select two features that belong to the Italian Renaissance tradition and two features that belong to the northern Gothic tradition.

Renaissance	Northern Gothic

7. Name three symbols in Dürer's etching *Knight, Death, and the Devil*, and tell what each symbol represents.

8. What religious conflicts and tension did Dürer experience during his life that influenced his etching?

Name ____________________ Date ____________ Class Period ________

9. What did Dürer study in Italian painting that he applied to his own art? ____________________

10. How do Bosch's paintings reflect the times in which he lived? ____________________

11. Describe two details of Bosch's *Death and the Miser* (page 420) that reveal his storytelling skill and his sense of humor.

12. In what way(s) did Pieter Bruegel carry on Bosch's storytelling tradition? ____________________

13. Study Bruegel's *The Parable of the Blind*, and tell why it is more similar to the northern style begun by Jan van Eyck, rather than to Renaissance artists.

14. Locate the axis line of the figures in *The Parable of the Blind*. How does this line enhance the story line in the painting?

15. Who was the German artist who became a painter for King Henry VIII of England? For what kind of paintings did this artist become famous?

16. Why is the painting of *Edward VI as a Child* significant as a work of art that reflects a specific time in English history?

17. Explain how Holbein's portrait of Anne of Cleves became an important part of history.

STUDY GUIDE 44

Name ______________________ Date ____________ Class Period ______

Part 1

Directions Explore styles in architecture and sculpture during the Counter-Reformation and answer the following questions.

1. What was the Counter-Reformation and where was it centered during the late sixteenth and early seventeenth centuries?

____

____

2. Describe the role of art during the Counter-Reformation by listing the goals the Church hoped to achieve through art.

____

____

3. How did the Counter-Reformation movement affect architectural design? ____________

____

____

4. Name two Baroque churches in Rome and note a design feature of each. ____________

____

____

5. List three characteristics of Baroque sculpture. ____________

____

____

6. What is most striking about the ceiling fresco in Sant' Ignazio, Rome, Italy (Figure 19.4, page 432)?

____

____

7.. What theory of art do you think was most important to the Baroque artists? ____________

____

8. What two artistic qualities were shared by all Baroque works of art? ____________

____

____

Name ______________________ Date ______________ Class Period ________

9. Study *The Conversion of St. Paul* on page 435 and tell what characteristics in Caravaggio's painting are considered Baroque.

____

____

10. What unique role did Artemisia Gentileschi play in the history of art? ______________

____

____

11. Which five artists influenced the work of Rubens, and what did he learn from each of them?

____

____

____

____

____

Part 2

Directions Complete the activities and respond to the questions in the spaces provided.

12. Study the painting *Daniel in the Lions' Den* by Rubens (page 438), and enhance your perception of Rubens's work by completing the design chart below.

		Principles of Art						
		Balance	Emphasis	Harmony	Variety	Gradation	Movement/ Rhythm	Proportion
Elements of Art	Color: Hue							
	Intensity							
	Value							
	Value (Non-Color)							
	Line							
	Texture							
	Shape/Form							
	Space							

Name ______________________ Date ____________ Class Period ________

13. Which elements and principles seem to be most important to Rubens? Name them, and give examples from the painting to illustrate your choices.

____

____

14. Having used the design chart to study the picture *Daniel in the Lions' Den,* describe three details that typify the Baroque style.

____

____

STUDY GUIDE 45

Name ______________________ Date ____________ Class Period ______

Directions Learn about several important Dutch painters as you read Section 2 and complete the questions in the spaces provided.

1. After 1658, why were Dutch painters searching for new subject matter for art? ______

2. What were genre paintings? ______

3. Why did artists begin to specialize in their choice of subject matter? ______

4. For what subject matter was Frans Hals known? ______

5. Which of Rembrandt's artistic achievements is dramatically demonstrated in *The Night Watch*?

6. Describe *Artist in His Studio* as if you were writing to someone who cannot see it. Write about the style and feeling as well as the content.

7. Which artists in the section were part of the group known as the "Little Dutch Masters"?

8. What qualities characterize the paintings of the "Little Dutch Masters"? ______

9. Examine the picture of Jan Steen's painting *Eve of St. Nicholas,* and describe the literal details in the composition that show Steen is telling about an event.

Name ______________________ Date ____________ Class Period ______

10. Show how Steen organized the composition of *Eve of St. Nicholas* to help the viewer follow the story. In the rectangle below, diagram the composition. Use straight lines to trace the path of movement Steen planned. Use circles to indicate the areas of emphasis—the places your eyes stop to examine.

11. How does Steen create the depth in the room? ______________________

____

____

12. Although Steen's work is Dutch and secular, what characteristics do you find in it that are similar to the style of Caravaggio or Rubens?

____

____

STUDY GUIDE 46

Name ____________________ Date __________ Class Period ______

Directions Evaluate the artwork of Spanish Baroque painters and answer the questions in the spaces provided.

1. How did the art subjects of Holland differ from those of Spain during the seventeenth century?

____

____

2. How was the Spanish artist Jusepe de Ribera influenced by Caravaggio? ____

____

____

3. Compare and contrast the work of Rubens and Jusepe de Ribera. Name some important similarities and differences.

____

____

4. Velázquez skillfully tells a story of military victory in his painting *Surrender of Breda*. Describe at least three details in the painting that tell the viewer which side was victorious.

____

____

5. How has Velázquez opened up the space in the painting *Las Meninas (The Maids of Honor)*? Describe at least two examples.

____

____

6. Velázquez and Murillo led very different lives. How are their backgrounds reflected in the two examples of these artists' works? (See pages 449–453.)

____

____

Name ______________________ Date ______________ Class Period ________

7. Make a diagram of the Murillo painting *The Return of the Prodigal Son* in the space below. Use only straight lines to indicate the direction the figures seem to be leading or pointing.

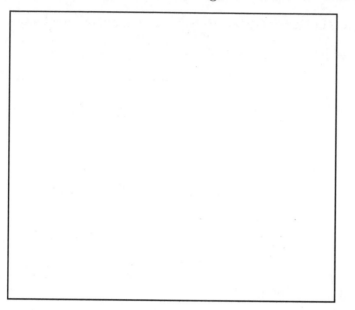

8. How does Murillo focus the viewer's attention on the reunion of father and son in this complex composition?

____

____

9. What was the effect of the religious division of Europe on the artists of the seventeenth century?

____

____

STUDY GUIDE 47

Name _______________ Date _______________ Class Period _______

Directions Compare Baroque and Rococo art and the influence of the French aristocracy, as you read Section 1. Then answer the questions in the space provided.

1. Which French king initiated the building of the Palace of Versailles? What was his nickname?

2. What is the meaning of the word *rococo*, and why was it used to describe the art style of the eighteenth century?

3. Contrast the style and philosophy of Rococo and Baroque art by describing some of their differences.

4. Explain how the literal and design elements of Watteau's *Embarkation for Cythera* (page 461) relate to the expressive quality of his work.

5. How did Fragonard achieve unity in his painting *The Swing* (Figure 20.6, page 463), showing his skills as a master designer?

6. Compare Watteau's work to that of Fragonard.

7. What are some of the characteristics of decorative accessories and furniture of the Rococo period?

8. How did Chardin elevate the objects and activities of common people?

Name _______________ Date _______________ Class Period _______

9. Look at Chardin's painting *The Attentive Nurse* (page 464). Complete the design chart operation by noting the characteristics of this painting in the appropriate spaces.

		Principles of Art						
		Balance	Emphasis	Harmony	Variety	Gradation	Movement/ Rhythm	Proportion
Elements of Art	Color: Hue							
	Intensity							
	Value							
	Value (Non-Color)							
	Line							
	Texture							
	Shape/Form							
	Space							

10. Which art elements are most important in this painting? How are the principles applied to those elements? Describe how these elements and principles work in the painting.

____

____

11. Although this painting was done in the period called Rococo, it is characteristic, in many ways, of the earlier genre paintings of the Baroque period. What aspects of this painting are more like the earlier Baroque genre paintings?

____

____

Name ______________________ Date ____________ Class Period ______

Part 1

Directions As you read about the art of eighteenth-century England and Spain, answer the questions in the spaces provided.

1. Who supported the arts in England in the eighteenth century and what kind of art was popular?

2. What made Sir Joshua Reynolds one of the first popular English portrait artists?

3. Explain the relationship between Reynolds and Gainsborough. Include the reasons for Gainsborough's painting *The Blue Boy*.

4. Do you think *The Blue Boy* is a successful work of art? Why or why not?

5. Explain how the art of Hogarth differs from the art of Reynolds and Gainsborough.

6. Name the Hogarth picture mentioned in your textbook in which Hogarth satirized a custom. Tell what aspects of the painting reveal the artist's tone and purpose.

7. Why were so many churches built and designed in London in the late seventeenth and early eighteenth centuries?

8. What was Christopher Wren known for as an accomplished architect?

Name ______________________ Date ____________ Class Period ______

9. St. Paul's Cathedral in London is one of Wren's most famous buildings. Describe several of its features.

____

____

Part 2

Directions Answer the questions in the spaces provided.

10. Study Francisco Goya's two paintings on pages 469 and 470 and the aquatint on page 472. Complete the chart below. Contrast the subject matter, composition, and aesthetic qualities of these three artworks.

	Title of Work	Subject Matter	Characteristics of Work
a.			
b.			
c.			

11. Using the steps in the art-criticism operation, complete the chart below for one of Goya's works.

Title: ____

Description	Analysis	Interpretation	Judgment

12. Of the three pieces by Goya, which do you prefer and why? ______________________

____

____

13. Why is Goya regarded as the bridge between art of the past and art of the present?

____

____

STUDY GUIDE 48a

Name ______________________ Date ____________ Class Period ________

Directions As you read Section 1, examine the development of the Neoclassic art style and respond to the following questions.

1. Explain the origin and importance of the Salon. ______________________

2. What are some of the reasons for the revival of interest in the classical art of Rome and Greece?

3. Jacques Louis David managed to combine his love of classical art, his skill as a painter, and his political beliefs in his painting *The Death of Marat* pictured on page 482. Explain how this painting makes a political statement.

4. If you were to commission Vigée-Lebrun to paint your portrait, what would you expect?

5. Relate the events that led Ingres to become the leader of the Neoclassic movement in France.

6. Why is Ingres's portrait of *Madame Moitessier* a good example of the Neoclassic style?

7. What element of art was most important in Ingres's work? ______________________

8. What qualities of classical and Neoclassical art have inspired the contemporary artist Mariani?

STUDY GUIDE 49

Name ______________________ Date ____________ Class Period ______

Part 1

Directions Examine the characteristics and themes of the Romantic and Realist styles, and respond to the following questions.

1. What are the major differences between Romanticism and Neoclassicism? ______

2. List four elements in Géricault's *Raft of the Medusa* (page 487) that mark the break with Neoclassicism.

3. Which art style that you have previously studied is similar to the Romantic style in philosophy?

4. What two experiences influenced the art of Delacroix? ______

5. What was the reason for the conflict between Ingres and Delacroix? ______

6. Study Delacroix's painting *The Lion Hunt* (page 488) by completing the design chart below.

		Principles of Art						
		Balance	Emphasis	Harmony	Variety	Gradation	Movement/ Rhythm	Proportion
Elements of Art	Color: Hue							
	Intensity							
	Value							
	Value (Non-Color)							
	Line							
	Texture							
	Shape/Form							
	Space							

Name ____________________ Date __________ Class Period ______

7. What element of art was considered most important to Delacroix? ____________________

8. Discuss Delacroix's use of that element in *The Lion Hunt*. Describe details from the painting that support your answer.

Part 2

Directions Respond to the activities and questions in the spaces provided.

9. How was Constable's approach to painting landscapes similar to that of the seventeenth-century Dutch masters?

10. How do Joseph M. W. Turner's landscapes compare with those of Constable? ____________________

11. Why were Turner's works criticized? ____________________

12. Complete the art-history operation for Turner's *Snow Storm: Steam-Boat off a Harbor's Mouth* (page 491).

Art-History Operations			
Description	**Analysis**	**Interpretation**	**Judgment**

Name ______________________ Date ____________ Class Period ______

13. Use the information you have gathered to decide on the importance of this work. Is *Snow Storm: Steam-Boat off a Harbor's Mouth* an important work in art history? Tell why or why not.

14. What changes in society prompted the new style of art called Realism?

15. What unspoken rule did Courbet break with his painting *Burial at Ornans*?

16. What theory of art (see page 493) is most evident in Courbet's painting *Burial at Ornans*?

17. What was the major difference between the art of Courbet and Manet?

18. Review Manet's painting *Gare Saint-Lazare*, page 494. Then answer the following questions.
    - **a.** Is the balance in this painting symmetrical or asymmetrical? ______
    - **b.** In what ways has the artist achieved variety? ______
    - **c.** How is unity achieved in this painting? How has the artist tied the various parts together?

19. What was the favorite subject of Rosa Bonheur? ______

20. How did Bonheur combine Romanticism and Realism in her painting *The Horse Fair*?

STUDY GUIDE 50

Name ______________________ Date ____________ Class Period ______

Directions Read about the goals and techniques of Impressionist artists as you answer the questions in the spaces provided.

1. What were the artistic concerns and goals of the Impressionist painters? ______________________

2. What two means did the Impressionists use to accomplish their artistic goals? ______________________

3. Why were they first called "Impressionists"? ______________________

4. What angered critics most about Monet's *Haystacks*? ______________________

5. Explain how and why Monet made so many paintings of the same subjects. ______________________

6. How does the work of Renoir reflect the style of Impressionism? ______________________

7. What were the two major influences on the work of the Impressionists? ______________________

8. List three qualities in the Japanese prints that appealed to the Impressionists. ______________________

9. How did photography affect the composition of the paintings of the Impressionists? ______________________

Name ______________________ Date ____________ Class Period ________

10. Study Degas's painting *The Glass of Absinthe* on page 501. Which details are influenced by the Japanese prints?

11. Which details are influenced by photography?

12. What artistic interest set Degas apart from other Impressionists?

13. What were the favorite subjects of Degas?

14. How did Mary Cassatt become an Impressionist?

15. Explain the composition in Mary Cassatt's painting *Girl Arranging Her Hair* (page 502).

16. Both Degas and Cassatt suffered loss of vision as they aged. How did each manage to remain involved with art?

17. Which painting technique did Morisot employ to capture the natural expression of her models?

18. Compare the sculptures of Rodin to the paintings of the Impressionists.

STUDY GUIDE 51

Name ________ Date ________ Class Period ________

Part 1

Directions As you read Section 1 and identify Post-Impressionist artists, answer the following questions in the spaces provided.

1. What were some of the concerns of the Post-Impressionist artists?

2. Who were three important Post-Impressionist painters?

3. What was Giotto's style of art that Cézanne challenged?

4. What did Cézanne do that was so different?

5. Study Cézanne's painting *Pines and Rocks (Fontainebleau?)*, Figure 22.3 on page 513. Describe the technique he used to create images in this painting.

6. Why did Cézanne focus on still-life arrangements and landscapes as his subjects?

7. What characterizes Cézanne's landscapes and still lifes?

8. Compare Cézanne's *Still Life with Peppermint Bottle* (page 512) with the still life by Chardin, Figure 20.7 on page 463. The ingredients of the picture are very similar: food, containers, and draped cloth. Describe, in your own words, the ways in which these pictures are different in technique and in overall effect.

Name ______________________ Date ____________ Class Period ______

9. Study the Cézanne painting *Pines and Rocks (Fontainebleau?)* by completing the chart below, according to the art-history method.

Art-History Operations			
Description	**Analysis**	**Interpretation**	**Judgment**

10. Is this painting one that is significant in the history of art? Why? ______________________

____

____

Part 2

Directions As you read about the work of van Gogh, respond to the following questions.

11. Look at the paintings by Vincent van Gogh (pages 514-516) and describe what you observe about his style of painting. Compare it with the style of Cézanne. What are the similarities and differences?

____

____

____

____

12. How does van Gogh create the somber mood in his painting *The Potato Eaters* (page 514)? Which art element is used most prominently to portray the emotional content of the painting?

____

____

13. How did seeing the Japanese woodcut prints influence van Gogh's painting? Describe the influences that are visible in his painting *The Bedroom at Arles* (page 515).

____

____

Name ____________________ Date ____________ Class Period ______

14. Begin your study of *The Starry Night* (page 516) by making notes in the theories-of-art chart below.

	Theories of Art		
	Imitationalism	Formalism	Emotionalism
Aesthetic Qualities	Literal Qualities: (Realistic presentation of subject matter)	Design Qualities: (Elements and principles)	Expressive Qualities: (Moods, feelings, and ideas)

15. Which theory of art do you think was most important to van Gogh? Explain your answer by referring to elements in the painting *The Starry Night*.

____

____

Part 3

Directions Answer the questions in the spaces below. Study Gauguin's painting *Fatata te Miti* (page 518) by examining the elements of art that seem to be important in his painting and by discovering how they were used.

16. What change in life style did Gauguin make for his art? ______________________________

____

17. Where was Gauguin living when he did his most important paintings? ______________________________

____

Name ______________________ Date ____________ Class Period ________

18. Complete the design chart by checking the elements and principles that apply to the painting *Fatata te Miti.*

Elements of Art		Principles of Art						
		Balance	Emphasis	Harmony	Variety	Gradation	Movement/ Rhythm	Proportion
	Color: Hue							
	Intensity							
	Value							
	Value (Non-Color)							
	Line							
	Texture							
	Shape/Form							
	Space							

19. How does Gauguin use art elements in *Fatata te Miti* to produce a decorative pattern?

____

____

20. How was Gauguin's view of art and nature similar to Cézanne's even though their works look very different?

____

____

STUDY GUIDE 52

Name ______________________ Date ____________ Class Period ______

Part 1

Directions As you examine the art of the late nineteenth century in America, answer the questions in the spaces provided.

1. How are the paintings of Homer and Eakins similar? ______________________

2. What kinds of subjects did Homer paint during his career as an illustrator and as a painter?

3. Which artists and teachers influenced the painting style of Thomas Eakins? ______________________

4. What did critics say about Homer and about Eakins? Do you agree or disagree? Tell why.

5. Which of the paintings that you have previously studied would you choose as a good comparison to Eakins's *The Gross Clinic*? Indicate your choice, the page number, and why you made that choice.

   Title: ______________________ Page: __________

   Why? ______________________

6. How was the work and life of Albert Pinkham Ryder completely different from the lives and works of Eakins and Homer?

7. Who was Joshua Johnston, and why is his place in art history changing? ______________________

8. What was the important achievement of the black painter Edward Bannister? ______________________

Name ______ Date ______ Class Period ______

9. Who was Henry Tanner's teacher? ______

10. Why did Henry Tanner move to Europe in the 1890s, ignoring the advice of his teacher? ______

Part 2

Directions Review the theories of art in the chart below. Make mental notes of the components of each theory. Next, study the following artworks in the chapter, and decide which theory of art best suits that example. Then write a brief explanation of your answer, using examples from that painting to support your choice.

	Theories of Art		
	Imitationalism	Formalism	Emotionalism
Aesthetic Qualities	Literal Qualities: **Realistic presentation** of subject matter.	Design Qualities: **Effective organization** of the elements of art through the use of the principles of art.	Expressive Qualities: **Vivid communication** of moods, feelings, and ideas.

11. Winslow Homer, *The Fog Warning* (page 521) ______

12. Thomas Eakins, *The Gross Clinic* (page 522) ______

13. Albert Pinkham Ryder, *Jonah* (page 523) ______

14. Henry Tanner, *The Banjo Lesson* (page 525) ______

15. Edmonia Lewis, *Forever Free* (page 526) ______

Name ______________________ Date ______________ Class Period ______

Part 1

Directions Examine the art of the early twentieth century and answer the following questions in the spaces provided.

1. Who was the leader of the so-called Fauves? ______________________

2. Describe the style of the Fauves. ______________________

3. What was the origin of the nickname "Fauves" for these painters? ______________________

4. Explain the way each of these Post-Impressionist painters influenced the Fauves.
   - a. van Gogh ______________________
   - b. Gauguin ______________________

Part 2

Directions Look at Matisse's painting *The Red Studio* (page 534) and answer the following questions.

5. What purpose is served by the intense red hue? ______________________

6. How does Matisse manage to invite the viewer into the studio? ______________________

7. In addition to color, what art elements are most important to Matisse? ______________________

8. What was Matisse's goal in creating his art? ______________________

9. How does Matisse create unity in *The Red Studio*? ______________________

10. Later in his life, how did Matisse further simplify his work? Describe how he worked. ______________________

Name ______________________ Date __________ Class Period ______

11. What did Matisse believe was the purpose of art? ______________________

12. Contrast the ideas and styles of Rouault and Matisse. What view of art did they share? ______________________

13. What two purposes were served by the strong black outlines in Rouault's painting *The Old King*?

Part 3

Directions Answer the questions from your reading and from studying the art examples.

14. What social condition does Kirchner portray in *Street, Berlin* (Figure 23.5)? ______________________

15. Explain how Kirchner's ideas and temperament affected his art and his life. ______________________

16. In what art media did Käthe Kollwitz work? ______________________

17. Which artists influenced Kollwitz's work? ______________________

18. In what way is Edvard Munch's painting *The Sick Child* autobiographical? ______________________

19. Think about the styles of the Fauves and the Expressionists. If you were a painter and had to choose to follow one style or the other, which would you prefer? Why?

20. What is the importance of the work of Wassily Kandinsky in the history of art? ______________________

Name ______________________ Date ____________ Class Period ______

21. Study Kandinsky's painting *Improvisation 28 (Second Version)* on page 539 and make notes in the chart below.

	Theories of Art		
	Imitationalism	**Formalism**	**Emotionalism**
Aesthetic Qualities	Literal Qualities:	Design Qualities:	Expressive Qualities:

22. Which theory of art does Kandinsky demonstrate in this painting? Explain your answer.

____

____

Part 4

Directions Read the text and answer the questions in the spaces provided.

23. Which Post-Impressionist artist prepared the way for Cubism? ______________________________

____

24. Describe the ideas of the Cubists about the following art elements.

a. line ______________________________

b. space ______________________________

c. shape ______________________________

d. color ______________________________

25. Why is the technique of collage associated with Cubism? ______________________________

____

____

Name ______________________ Date ______________ Class Period ________

26. Is Cubism a result of an emotional or an intellectual process? Explain your answer. ______________

27. Describe how Picasso combined Expressionism and Cubism in his painting *Guernica* (page 541). Locate specific examples of each style within the work.

28. What is one of the most significant differences between the two careers of Picasso and Braque?

29. In what ways is the sculpture of Aristide Maillol related to the still lifes of Braque? What classical characteristics do they share?

30. Which shapes unify the composition of the sculpture *The Mediterranean* by Maillol on page 543?

STUDY GUIDE 54

Name ______________________ Date __________ Class Period ______

Directions As you read Section 2, identify the Mexican muralists and the American artists of the early twentieth century. Then answer the questions and complete the activities in the spaces provided.

1. What precedent was revived by the Mexican muralists? ______________________

2. List four subjects painted by the Mexican muralists. ______________________

3. What did the mural painters hope to accomplish by painting on public walls? ______________________

4. Write the names of three famous Mexican muralists in Chapter 23 and note special features that distinguish each style.

5. What was happening in the American art world at the turn of the century? ______________________

6. Study John Sloan's painting *Backyards, Greenwich Village* on page 548. Describe how he guides the viewer's eyes around the painting.

7. What was George Bellows's favorite subject? What is characteristic of his paintings?

8. Why were the group of artists, including John Sloan, labeled the Ashcan School?

Name ______________________ Date ____________ Class Period ______

9. Study George Bellows's painting *Stag at Sharkey's* (page 549). Take notes in the chart below as you did with the Kandinsky example earlier in the chapter.

	Theories of Art		
	Imitationalism	Formalism	Emotionalism
Aesthetic Qualities	Literal Qualities:	Design Qualities:	Expressive Qualities:

10. Which theory of art is most relevant, in your mind, to *Stag at Sharkey's*? Describe the details in the painting that influenced your choice.

____

____

11. What is the most significant difference between Bellows's *Stag at Sharkey's* (page 549) and Kandinsky's *Improvisation 28* (page 539)?

____

____

12. The two paintings, however, share a significant similarity. Study both paintings and tell what characteristic they have in common.

____

13. What was the Armory Show of 1913, and why was it held? ____________________

____

14. Why was the reaction of the Americans to the Armory Show so different from that of Europeans?

____

____

15. What was the result of the Armory Show among American artists? ____________________

____

STUDY GUIDE 55

Name ______________________ Date ______________ Class Period ________

Directions Explore architectural styles in Europe and America and answer the questions in the spaces provided.

1. What late nineteenth- and early twentieth-century developments enabled architects to consider changes in traditional architectural designs?

2. Tell what materials were utilized for the Eiffel Tower in Paris and describe how it was built.

3. What was Gaudi's philosophy of architecture?

4. Study the photos of Gaudi's Güell Park (Figure 23.26 on page 552). Describe his style by finding three adjectives that are appropriate to describe it.

5. What is Julia Morgan's most famous architectural achievement?

6. Describe Morgan's attitude about her work and her reputation.

7. What American architect is credited with initiating the International Style?

8. Describe his design for the Wainwright Building in St. Louis, pictured on page 555.

9. List three features of the International Style of architecture.

STUDY GUIDE 56

Name ________________ Date ________ Class Period ______

Directions Explore twentieth-century art movements and answer the following questions.

1. What is Dada art? What were the general social, economic, and political conditions at the time the Dada art movement began?

2. Why is the painting *Carnival of Harlequin* by Joan Miró considered a Surrealist painting?

3. What are some differences between the Surrealist paintings of Miró and Salvador Dali?

4. Although Klee's paintings are filled with fantasy, how does his work differ from those of the Surrealists?

5. Name and describe a Surrealist painting by an American artist.

6. In what ways was Regionalism a contrast to Surrealism?

7. Choose a Regionalist painting from this chapter. Then write the title and the artist, and list examples from that painting that indicate what the artist communicated.

Name ______________________ Date ______________ Class Period ______

8. Complete the chart below to compare the subjects these four artists painted and how they sought new ways of looking at those subjects.

	Artist	Subject/Technique
a.	Stuart Davis	
b.	Georgia O'Keeffe	
c.	Alice Neel	
d.	Jacob Lawrence	

9. What were at least four characteristics of Abstract Expressionism?

____

____

____

____

10. Compare four Abstract Expressionist artists by completing the chart below.

	Artist	Work of Art	Subject/Technique
a.	Motherwell		
b.			expression of feeling through the physical act of painting, unplanned
c.			thinned paint poured on unprimed canvas, flowing, graceful, free-form shapes
d.	de Kooning		

STUDY GUIDE 57

Name ______________________ Date ____________ Class Period ______

Part 1

Directions Identify twentieth-century sculptors and architects and answer the following questions.

1. How did twentieth-century sculptors search for new forms? Give a few examples.

2. Describe three ways in which the artworks of Henry Moore and Barbara Hepworth are similar.

3. Tell how Lipchitz's *Sailor with Guitar* (page 572) reflects the painting style of Cubism.

4. What art element is very evident in Houser's *Watching for Dancing Partners* (page 572)? Describe the ways that element is used in this sculpture.

5. Define *mobile* (as it is used to denote a work of art), and describe a mobile by Alexander Calder.

6. What kinds of sculpture did Louise Nevelson create? What were her materials?

7. Contrast the style and materials of Nevelson's sculpture with Duane Hanson's sculpture.

Part 2

Directions Answer the following questions, going back to the text when necessary.

8. Describe three features of the architecture of Notre Dame du Haute that differ from the International Style.

Name ______________________ Date ____________ Class Period ________

9. Frank Lloyd Wright and I. M. Pei each designed an important art museum for a major U.S. city. In the space provided, tell the name of the museum, the city, and describe a special design feature.

   a. Frank Lloyd Wright

      Museum: ______________________ City ____________

      Design Feature: ______________________

   b. I. M. Pei

      Museum: ______________________ City ____________

      Design Feature: ______________________

10. Name a major contribution to twentieth-century architecture made by each of these architects:

    a. Le Corbusier ______________________

    b. Frank Lloyd Wright ______________________

    c. I. M. Pei ______________________

11. What is unique about Maya Lin's Vietnam Veterans Memorial? ______________________

    ____

12. Select a work of architecture and a work of sculpture from this chapter. Then compare at least three elements of art for the works you selected. (You may want to review Chapter 2.)

	Art Element	Architecture	Sculpture
a.			
b.			
c.			

Name ______ Date ______ Class Period ______

Part 3

Directions Answer the following questions, going back to the text when necessary.

13. List four new art movements that have challenged Abstract Expressionism.

______

______

______

______

14. What did the British Pop artists select for materials to create a message with their collages?

______

______

15. Name two Pop artists and tell what you think each was trying to communicate. ______

______

______

16. Define Op art. Tell where this movement began. ______

______

______

17. Name two Op artists and briefly describe the work of each.

a. ______

b. ______

18. Name five major features of the style known as Hard-edge painting.

______

______

______

______

______

19. What is Photo-Realism and when did it become a leading art style?

______

______

Name ______________________ Date ______________ Class Period ______

20. Why is the work of Alfred Leslie compared to Caravaggio's painting?

21. a. Name three objects Audrey Flack included in her painting *Marilyn* (page 451).

b. Explain why you think the artist selected those particular objects.

22. Why are the works of Andrew Wyeth not classified as Photo-Realism?

23. Study the Wyeth painting *Winter, 1946* (page 580) and tell how it may be autobiographical.

24. Who were the Canadian Group of Seven? ______________________

25. Compare the ideas of Emily Carr and Georgia O'Keeffe. In what ways do they resemble one another?

Study Guide 1 (Chapter 1, Section 1)

1. **(a)** Describe. Explain what is in the work.
   (b) Analyze. Explain how the work is organized or put together.
   (c) Interpret. Explain what ideas or feelings are communicated.
   (d) Judge. Determine the artistic merit of the artwork.
2. **(a)** Describe. Find out who did the work, where it was done, and when it was done.
   (b) Analyze. Identify the unique features of the artwork.
   (c) Interpret. Explain how the artwork was influenced by the time in which it was created.
   (d) Judge. Explain its importance in the history of art.
3. You can check the ideas you had in the art-criticism steps. You may gain more knowledge and change your judgment.
4. aesthetician
5. imitationalists
6. formalists
7. emotionalists
8. art patron
9. practical
10. fine art

Study Guide 2 (Chapter 1, Section 2)

1. corporate art adviser
2. photojournalist
3. advertising artist
4. graphic designer
5. computer graphics artist
6. arts administrator
7. fashion designer
8. architects
9. Any four: shrubs, trees, flowers, rivers, ponds, walks, benches, signs.
10. A college education (four-year degree) that includes preparation in art and education.
11. Tombs, sculpture, pottery, tools, weapons, and building foundations unearthed to learn how ancient people lived.
12. They are responsible for securing and exhibiting artworks for the general public and scholars to view.
13. **(a)** Keep a sketchbook and practice drawing on a daily basis.
    (b) Develop a portfolio of ideas, works-in-progress, and finished pieces.
    (c) Study the artworks of the masters for inspiration as well as to see how they have used various media and expressed their ideas.

Study Guide 3 (Chapter 2, Section 1)

1. color, value, line, texture, shape, form, and space
2. balance, emphasis, harmony, variety, gradation, movement, rhythm, and proportion
3. Reference to the special way an artist uses the elements and principles to organize a work.
4. **(a)–(g)** Answers will vary according to the object chosen by each student.
5. hue, intensity, value
6. Intensity refers to the brightness or purity of a color. Value refers to a color's darkness or lightness.
7. (Diagram)
8. (Diagram)
9. Drawings, woodcuts, lithographs, and photographs.
10. Abrupt value changes indicate plane changes. Gradual value change suggests gently curved surfaces.

Study Guide 4 (Chapter 2, Section 2)

1. **(a)** suggests strength and stability
   (b) suggests calmness
   (c) suggests tension
   (d) an imaginary line used to trace direction of movement
   (e) shows the edges of an object; an outline

2. **(a)** surface textures like satin or plaster are simulated, yet the surface of the painting is smooth.
   (b) actual rough and smooth surfaces can be felt on the sculpture.
3. color, value, line, texture, and space
4. A shape is flat and is limited to two dimensions. A form is an object with three dimensions.
5. Answers may vary, but should refer to (1) overlapping shapes; (2) making distant shapes smaller and closer shapes larger; (3) with color, distance is created by using less intense hues; (4) placing distant shapes higher and closer shapes lower; (5) perspective is shown by slanting the horizontal lines of shapes to make them appear to extend back into space.
6. Three-dimensional space is actual space related to three-dimensional forms having height, width, and depth. Space is two-dimensional in works that have only height and width and no actual depth or distance.

Study Guide 5 (Chapter 2, Section 3)

1. stability or equilibrium
2. symmetrical; asymmetrical
3. emphasis
4. harmony
5. variety
6. gradual changes
7. movement
8. rhythm
9. proportion
10. rhythm
11. balance
12. To help identify relationships between the elements of art and principles of art.

Study Guide 6 (Chapter 3, Section 1)

1. pencil, charcoal, crayon, chalk, pastels
2. Wet media are those in which the coloring agent is suspended in a liquid and include ink and paint.
3. as preliminary sketches for their paintings and sculptures
4. as a finished work of art and as preliminary studies from which to develop ideas
5. It enables the artist to record ideas suggested by daily observations and experiences.
6. **(a)** portrait
   (b) still life
   (c) historical
   (d) landscape
   (e) dreams/imaginary
   (f) animals
   (g) religious

Study Guide 7 (Chapter 3, Section 2)

1. Chinese artists
2. He perfected the printing press.
3. relief, intaglio, lithography, screen printing
4. relief
5. intaglio
6. etching
7. lithography
8. serigraph
9. subject, light conditions, point of view, and creative work done in the darkroom
10. Alfred Stieglitz, Ansel Adams, Imogen Cunningham, Man Ray

Study Guide 8 (Chapter 4, Section 1)

1. Sculpture exists in actual space; a three-dimensional form. Painting may give the illusion of space, but it is two-dimensional.
2. Bas relief and high relief. Bas relief is low relief, in which forms project only slightly from the background. High relief occurs when sculptured forms extend boldly out into space.
3. Freestanding sculpture surrounded on all sides by space.
4. clay, wood, marble, bronze, stone, metal

5. Answers will vary but should mention the qualities of marble and bronze: texture, color, pattern. These affect harmony, balance, emphasis, movement.
6. Possible choice: Käthe Kollwitz's *In God's Hands,* Figure 4.4, page 80.
7. Imitationalism

Study Guide 9 (Chapter 4, Section 2)

1. Modeling is a process in which a soft, pliable material is built up and shaped. Clay, wax, and plaster.
2. The sculptor gradually adds more material to build a form.
3. The armature is a support system, usually metal, around which an artist builds a sculpture.
4. *cire-perdue*
5. **(a)** 4 **(f)** 9
   (b) 7 **(g)** 1
   (c) 10 **(h)** 2
   (d) 3 **(i)** 8
   (e) 5 **(j)** 6

Study Guide 10 (Chapter 5, Section 1)

1. describe, analyze, interpret, judge
2. An individual style consists of those characteristics that are unique to that individual's style. A group style consists of the characteristics used by all the members of a group.
3. The effect of the Impressionist pictures was soft, indistinct, and somewhat blurred, giving only the *impression* of the subject matter rather than the sharp detail.
4. Paint was applied in small spots and dabs; spots of color placed next to complementary colors to make them seem brighter; the effect of flickering sunlight in the painting technique; the choice of everyday subjects.
5. strong, pure colors; edges fuzzy and out of focus, with the important detail—the child's face—in clearer focus.
6. the strong, dark outlines
7. The art historian might be on the staff of a museum and may use the information for gallery notes or publications regarding the artwork.

Study Guide 11 (Chapter 5, Section 2)

Part 1

1. **(a)** judgment
   (b) interpretation
   (c) description
   (d) analysis
2. Internal cues are contained *in* the work; correlates with the art-criticism approach. External cues relate to the aspects that exist *outside* the work; correlates with the art-history approach.
3. Literal, design, expressive

Part 2

4. I 7. A
5. D 8. I
6. A 9. J

Part 3

10. There is no one "correct" way to interpret an artwork. It may be interpreted many different ways by different people.
11. Answers will vary.
12. Answers will vary.

Part 4

13. E
14. I or F; (I) The figures are quite lifelike, though the backdrop is stylized. (F) The arrangement of the figures is extremely formal and carefully designed.
15. I or F; (I) The objects are very lifelike, but (F) the arrangement is very formal.
16. F; A formal arrangement of the two elements color and line; no emotion or realism.
17. F; An entirely formal arrangement of lines, shapes, and colors.

Study Guide 12 (Chapter 5, Section 3)

Chart

Study Guide 13 (Chapter 6, Section 1)

1. Altamira
2. Answers will vary.
3. **(a)** rich, reddish hues
   (b) gradual value changes; contrasting values of smaller shapes
   (c) thick to thin dark lines as outline
   (d) three-dimensional mass of animal
   (e) rough stone surface
4. It will help you determine how the art elements are used.
5. Answers may vary, but should be accompanied by examples that support the choice.
6. Answers may vary, but should be accompanied by examples that support the choice.

Study Guide 14 (Chapter 6, Section 2)

1. 10,000 to 15,000
2. All living organisms maintain a known amount of radioactive carbon 14. After the organism's death, the carbon 14 loses its radioactivity at a known rate. By measuring how much radioactivity is left in the carbonized bones, it is possible to discover their age.
3. 30,000 B.C.; 10,000 B.C.
4. Two boys were playing with their dog; 1941. The dog disappeared in a hole when trying to retrieve a ball and became trapped in a cave.
5. The paint is applied in a way to achieve shading, so that the contours are more lifelike.
6. massive posts supporting crossbeams, or lintels.
7. by utilizing the natural contour of the stone for a three-dimensional effect
8. megaliths
9. post-and-lintel construction; circular arrangements of large upright stones

Study Guide 15 (Chapter 7, Section 1)

1. prehistoric hunters
2. fertile soil
3. Memphis
4. 500 years
5. law; order
6. New Kingdom
7. Thutmose III
8. Aton, one supreme god
9. the Old Kingdom
10. to confuse tomb robbers and enemies
11. (diagram)

Study Guide 16 (Chapter 7, Section 2)

1. If the pharaoh's body was stolen, the sculpted likeness could be used as a substitute by the ka to take to the next world.
2. The body is stiff and unnatural; the face is more relaxed and shows emotion.
3. probably Khafre; to show he has courage and strength of a lion
4. The expression is troubled and weary, not as strong and self-assured as Khafre.
5. Arts were encouraged. There were many commissioned artworks, and artists were active.
6. Because Nakht and his wife are much larger than the other figures, they are more important. Their stiff and solemn poses also indicate that they are people of high rank.
7. hieroglyphics

Study Guide 17 (Chapter 8, Section 1)

1. Mycenaeans and Dorians
2. Geography (separation by mountains, valleys, and seas) and rivalry
3. It was formed to pool the treasuries of the various city-states, so that they could defend themselves from invaders. The larger cities contributed ships and men; smaller cities gave money.
4. the Athenian leader who built the Parthenon
5. the great plague in 430 B.C.
6. a hill overlooking Athens on which were built some of the greatest examples of Greek architecture, including the Parthenon

7. because he used some of the funds from the Delian League, which were to have been used for defense
8. a. pediment
   b. frieze
   c. lintel
   d. capital
   e. column
   f. stylobate
9. Many of the marble surfaces were painted or covered with gold.
10. many temples; statues, including a huge statue of Athena; great flights of steps
11. (with sketch): shorter shaft, plain capital, no base on the shaft
12. (with sketch): longer shaft, capital in the shape of a double scroll
13. (with sketch): similar to the Ionic, but with an elongated capital in the shape of a bundle of leaves
14. The vases were covered with bands of simple geometric patterns. Eventually geometric figures were added.
15. The figures became more lifelike and were placed in storytelling scenes.
16. (a) *Kouros* is upright; *Discobolus* is in an athletic pose
    (b) *Kouros* seems static, stiff; *Discobolus* caught in motion
    (c) *Kouros* is rough; *Discobolus* smooth
    (d) *Kouros* is stylized; *Discobolus* naturalistic
17. bronze, so tall the tops of the spear could be seen by ships at sea
18. 42 feet (13 m) high, white marble, gold details on armor, gems for eyes and in crown
19. On the east frieze of the Parthenon.
20. Polyclitus creates a spiral axis that begins at the toes of the left foot and curves upward through the body to the head (contrapposto).
21. *Doryphorus*—Left leg is bent and toes lightly touch ground; weight is on right leg.
    Dying Gaul—There is an **S** curve from head to back to legs with weight on arm and hip.
    Seated Boxer—Head is turned up and away from the body; hands rest on one knee; shoulders are turned.

Study Guide 18 (Chapter 8, Section 2)

1. Archaic
2. Egyptian
3. Kouroi
4. Apollo
5. athlete
6. feet
7. spaces
8. arms, body
9. Korai
10. clothed
11. textures
12. cylinder
13. movement
14. early
15. Myron

Study Guide 19 (Chapter 9, Section 1)

1. An ancient people who first inhabited the land that is now Italy.
2. The Romans felt the face was the reflection of the personality and was sufficient to show character.
3. Imitationalism; portraits reflected all the wrinkles and imperfections.
4. Murals were often meant to simulate the view out a window of some outdoor scene.
5. Almost every house had wall paintings.
6. Greeks used freestanding columns to support roofs and upper floors. Romans often attached half columns to solid walls as decoration.
7. Placing it on a tall, raised platform.
8. The strength of the arch allowed wider spans to be supported.
9. the arch and concrete
10. the aqueduct in Segovia

Study Guide 20 (Chapter 9, Section 2)

1. The Baths were a social and cultural center. Like shopping centers today, they included gyms, shops, restaurants, and walkways, as well as libraries and lecture rooms.
2. Each story includes a different column style; lower is Doric, second is Ionic, and third is Corinthian.
3. The Pantheon was originally a temple devoted to all of the Roman gods.
4. Lower zone—Roman gods of the heavens; sun, moon, and five planets. Middle zone—twelve signs of the zodiac; the dome represented the heavens.
5. The dome looks low and shallow from the outside but is a perfect hemisphere inside.
6. Because they incorporate most of the architectural advances of the Romans in a single building. They became models for Christian church builders.
7. Returning victorious warriors were honored with parades through the arches with their troops.
8. The larger arch in the center was for the chariots, generals, mounted soldiers, etc. The smaller side arches were for the foot soldiers.
9. It was not built for the glorification of the military, has only one single arch, and does not feature sculptured reliefs.

Study Guide 21 (Chapter 10, Section 1)

1. bronze and copper technology, multistoried buildings of fired bricks, drainage system, written language of pictograms, commerce, central government, religion
2. Over a period of time, the Aryans blended their beliefs in many gods and goddesses with the Harappans' belief in many spirits.
3. **(a)** Brahma—creation
   (b) Vishnu—preservation
   (c) Shiva—destruction
4. A purification process in which the soul lives in many bodies over many lifetimes; the actions of one life influence those of another
5. Siddhartha Gautama; 500 B.C.
6. temples, monasteries (vihāras), and burial shrines (stupas)
7. Buddha was believed to have reached nirvana, and there was nothing to which such a person could be compared. Instead, symbols were used.
8. Human forms of Buddha, standing and seated cross-legged, convey great power with a feeling of inner peace.
9. Hindu temples served as a residence for a god. Buddhist temples served as a place for worshipers.
10. The dance symbolizes destruction and rebirth of the universe. Multiple arms: graceful movement; Drum: creation; Flame: destruction; Raised hand: protection of the faithful; Raised foot: escape from ignorance
11. The art of India was a reflection of religious beliefs. Buddhism and Hinduism spread to China and Japan, influencing the art of these countries as well.

Study Guide 22 (Chapter 10, Section 2)

1. bronzes, paintings
2. Answers may vary. Statues of the Buddha appeared. Other arts were infused with the calm and simplicity imposed by meditation. Art was regarded an honorable task.
3. Bodhisattva is a Buddha-to-be, someone who has attained a state of enlightenment or who returned from death to guide the living.
4. Chinese sculpture of the human figure represented religious significance. The Greeks considered the human body beautiful and their sculpture reflected this attitude.
5. Landscapes
6. Hanging scrolls were hung. Handscrolls were carefully rolled up, kept on shelves like books, and unrolled section by section to be observed.
7. Religious sculpture of Buddhas and clay tomb sculpture of animals.

8. Inscriptions and seals placed on paintings indicated that others, usually collectors, appreciated the skill of the artist.
9. Porcelain
10. It makes you feel that you are traveling through the scene.
11. Ceramics; the development of a beautiful cobalt-blue glaze.

Study Guide 23 (Chapter 10, Section 3)

1. In A.D. 552, a bronze Buddha, writings, and teachings were sent to Japan by the ruler of a kingdom in Korea.
2. Volcanic rock on the island of Japan is soft. Buildings need to withstand storms and earthquakes.
3. It is the oldest surviving wood structure in the world.
4. The pagodas contained sacred relics.
5. Heian; from 784 to 1185.
6. It means "painting in the Japanese manner." It was the beginning of a national style of art.
7. A growing, prosperous, middle class wanted art; printmaking enabled that demand to filled.
8. It means "pictures of the passing world." Printmaking.
9. Woodblock printing allowed the artist to produce many inexpensive prints, while paintings had to be created one at a time.
10. multicolor prints

Study Guide 24 (Chapter 11, Section 1)

1. land and sea animals: caribou, fox, wolf, and bear; seal, walrus, fish, and whale
2. Subjects: pictorial writing about everyday life such as the quest for food; Size: miniature; Materials: ivory pipestems colored with soot
3. Prosperity and leisure created by a vast food supply created ranks and subgroups among members. Dramatic initiation rituals for new members developed. Costumes and masks were made to show magical powers.
4. Ritual ceremony: wild, noisy, dramatic dance-like performances with elaborate costumes and masks for new clan members. Potlatch: an event hosted by one clan for another to show honor, rank, or status.
5. Tall posts, usually 30 to 50 feet (9 to 15 m) high with elaborately carved and painted details. Function: to identify a clan or family.
6. Adobe, or sun-dried clay, walls. Rooms were arranged in several stories, set in steplike fashion forming large terraces.
7. Eighteenth century: Spanish and Mexican settlers came and introduced new designs that Navajo weavers adopted. Nineteenth century: Navajos were using European cloth and dyes to create weavings of vibrant colors and bold designs.
8. The Blackfeet, Crow, Cheyenne, and Sioux were proficient in leatherwork, which was then painted or embroidered with quills and, later, beads.
9. The Adena artists managed to stylize the figure, show fully rounded form with a sturdy appearance, and make a functional pipe using primitive tools.
10. They represented the spirits who gave the healers their magic to treat illness.
11. Woodlands (Iroquois): carved wood, painted, decorated with horsehair and metal rings, considered sacred, represented spirit for healers' magical powers. Northwest (Hamatsa): several hinged pieces of carved wood so the features could appear to move, used for dramatic impact and to give the impression of supernatural power during initiation ceremonies of a society.

Study Guide 25 (Chapter 11, Section 2)

1. Unwelcome expressions: drooping mouth, peering eyes convey power.
2. Mayans believed the first people were formed by mixing maize, corn, and water and brought to life with the blood of the gods. They thought they had to repay this debt by returning blood to the gods.
3. Monuments and temples were placed around the plazas. Complex, intricate reliefs covered the buildings painted in red, blue, and green.

4. A.D. 320-1519. Spanish conquest by Cortés in 1519.
5. Huge white palaces, temples, and gardens. A system of irrigation canals and aqueducts was built on this island in Lake Texcoco.
6. They performed thousands of human sacrifices at the pyramid altars in the belief that it kept the gods in good spirits.
7. Large heads, short limbs, distorted poses and gestures, not representational images of human beings.
8. According to legend, Quetzalcóatl, the life god, would return from the East to redeem his people. When Cortés arrived from the East in 1519, the Aztecs thought he was their redeemer rather than their conqueror.
9. Although they had no written language the Incas built a network of roads and bridges. A series of relay runners used these roads and could relay messages to all parts of the empire.

Study Guide 26 (Chapter 12, Section 1)

1. copper-alloy castings
2. The casting techniques used were completely comparable to anything done in the West. It had been thought that only the European masters were capable of such techniques.
3. To decorate the pillars of the royal palace.
4. Answers will vary, but should point out: the arms thrust forward in space, giving a three-dimensional effect; the variety of textures and details, and symmetry of design.
5. copper alloy, iron, gold, and silver
6. Jewelry: necklaces, bracelets, anklets, and pendants
7. A measure of wealth. Worn by kings as a sign of divine authority and absolute power.
8. In the fifteenth century, an Ethiopian king decreed the wearing of crosses. These were made from iron or bronze. Since the nineteenth century, crosses have been made from silver.

Study Guide 27 (Chapter 12, Section 2)

Part 1

1. figures, masks, ceremonial items, furniture.
2. Humidity contributed to destruction of wood carvings. New masks had to be produced, with the result that the design was constantly improved.
3. little concern for natural proportions; frontal pose; enlarged heads; lack of movement
4. **(a)** ancestral; *Standing Female Figure* (Figure 12.10), *Chibinda (The Hunter)* (Figure 12.11)
   (b) power; *Magical Figure* (Figure 12.12), *Nhondc Nail Figure* (Figure 12.13)
   (c) funerary; *Reliquary Figure* (Figure 2.14)
5. **(a)** line, texture; wood; worn by dancer in farm ceremony
   (b) form, line, texture, value; wood, paint; worn at funeral of a chief
   (c) form, textures; wood; secret society that initiates young women into adult society

Study Guide 28 (Chapter 13, Section 1)

1. For burials and for hidden places to hold religious services.
2. Romans considered their earthly lives most important; Christians looked forward to life in the hereafter.
3. Answers will vary, but should point out that the early Christian art centered on Christ and used figures in stiff, pious poses (as in the picture on page 287) rather than in natural, lively actions.
4. His life was depicted to serve as a model for the way to salvation.
5. **(a)** Christ as the good shepherd
   (b) crown of thorns (goldfinches eat thistles)
   (c) immortality
   (d) faithfulness
   (e) eternal life
6. Exteriors were very plain and unadorned; interiors were elaborately decorated for dramatic effect.

7. They depicted stories from the Bible or symbols of Christian ideals.
8. Answers will vary, but should note the symmetrical arrangement of the figures around the central Madonna and Child and the poses that fit the shape of the half-circle niche rather than any natural action or pose.
9. Roman, Greek, Oriental
10. Byzantine art glorified the Christian religion and served the needs of the Church.
11. Walls could be thinner; more windows were possible for added light; the dome appeared lighter and higher.
12. Light from the windows illuminates the glass, marble, and precious stones of the mosaics, creating a spectacular effect.

Study Guide 29 (Chapter 13, Section 2)

1. The holy scriptures of Islam.
2. Mosque interiors: relief decorations of excerpts from the Koran. Christian interiors: many paintings, sculptures, and mosaics. Muhammad disapproved of painted or sculptured religious images or symbols. Christians viewed religious images as a way of teaching religion.
3. Similarities of these mosques: fortress palace, grouped rooms around a central patio or courtyard, fountains, ornate designs in the interior with inscriptions from the Koran.
4. Islamic artists avoided portraying living creatures because they did not want to diminish God's creative powers.
5. Rich, decorative effects and patterns.
6. By 1200 in Iraq and Iran.
7. Delicate flowing lines; shapes are flat; rich patterns; intense colors.

Study Guide 30 (Chapter 14, Section 1)

Part 1

1. Middle Ages
2. Medieval
3. Dark Ages
4. Dark Ages
5. Medieval
6. Romanesque
7. Gothic
8. Charlemagne
9. arts
10. Aix-la-Chapelle
11. Ravenna

Part 2

12. Weak central government and the need for protection.
13. Answers will vary but should follow the pattern described on page 313.
14. addition of the transept inside and towers outside
15. the shape of a cross made by the aisles
16. to form a religious community removed from "worldly" society
17. Answers will vary, but could include reference to monasteries, illuminations, bas reliefs.
18. positioned inside a huge cave, at the end of a narrow gorge
19. A book decorated with paintings in vivid colors, gold, and silver.
20. Answers will vary, but should mention the curved lines of the robe and background that give the picture vitality and motion.

Study Guide 31 (Chapter 14, Section 2)

Part 1

1. thick walls, lack of windows, moats, towers, drawbridges—all features designed for defense
2. changing economy, the rise of cities, land ownership became less important
3. growth of trade and industry with an economy based on money rather than land ownership
4. overcrowding; buildings were built on more than one floor with top floors often overhanging the street
5. A church in the center of town. It was the center for art, learning, and religion.

6. A journey to the holy place. Ideal pilgrimages were to the Holy Land or to Rome, but because of the dangers, medieval pilgrims usually journeyed to closer shrines.
7. extension of the nave and transept; small chapels built along the transept and the ambulatory; the ambulatory, or aisle, around the curve of the main altar.
8. how to construct a stone roof over the large churches
9. The barrel vault. No, even with great care taken, the walls sometimes collapsed from the weight.
10. Answers may include: rounded arches; small windows. Parts of the interior: nave, ambulatory, apse, transept, arches, barrel vaults, radiating chapels
11. Answers will vary. The figures are in rows of saints and sinners at the top—the saints upright and the sinners being pulled back to their doom.

Study Guide 32 (Chapter 15, Section 1)

1. Cities became stronger, more prosperous and the economy was based on money, not land. Promise of a better life in cities lured serfs away from their rural homes.
2. "Gothic" was the derisive name given to the style that replaced the Classical style of the Greeks and Romans, in reference to the fact that the barbarian Goths had defeated Rome.
3. No Goths ever built a cathedral.
4. **(a)** arches, pillars — flying buttresses
   (b) rounded — tall and pointed
   (c) simple — elaborate
   (d) candles, lamps — tinted sunlight through stained glass
5. Because they extended out from the walls and seemed to "fly."
6. It added support, eliminating the need for solid walls. More windows could be placed in the walls.
7. bright, glowing colors; dark lines separating colored areas
8. Minerals, which changed the color, were added to glass in its molten state. Small pieces were joined with lead strips to form patterns or pictures.
9. Funds came from planned and individual contributions. Clergy promised to pray for donors.

Study Guide 33 (Chapter 15, Section 2)

1. Answers may vary but should refer to the following: Gothic—upward tendency, elongated figures, vertical movement, figures project outward, more realism; Romanesque —figures firmly attached to wall, bas relief.
2. Christ is shown as a majestic, thoughtful, approachable man. The figures appear more three-dimensional.
3. Answers will vary, but should include the idea of serenity, warmth, comfort.
4. They were decorative rainspouts, carved like flying monsters. Reason and origin are unknown, but perhaps they represented evil spirits fleeing the church or were simply comical additions.
5. A style of painting—elegant, graceful, detailed, colorful.
6. A more realistic approach to painting, the inclusion of real people in the pictures, the grace and beauty of the designs, the brilliant jewellike colors.
7. Answers will vary but should include many of the factors in questions 5 and 6.
8. Psalter: an illustrated book of psalms, gospels, and liturgy showing the influence of stained-glass windows; flat, not realistic. "Book of Hours": an illustrated book of prayers (fifteenth century) with elaborate, detailed, realistic illustrations.
9. **(a)** May; France
   (b) unknown artist; England
10. The Art-History Operation chart should be completed with Chapter 5 as a guide.

Study Guide 34 (Chapter 15, Section 3)

Part 1

1. They preferred the Roman style, did not like the extensive use of windows.
2. Answers will vary; may include the "floating" figures, the gold background, the two-dimensional figures, intense colors.
3. Duccio's figures are more realistic, solid, detailed faces and gestures, more natural appearance.
4. A painting created with pigment applied to a wall spread with fresh plaster.
5. A charcoal drawing is done on a wall, the surface is painted with a thin coat of wet plaster and the charcoal lines are retraced. Paint is mixed with egg white and water and applied directly to the wet plaster.
6. Because the work must be done quickly, before the plaster dries, there is not time for intricate detail. Important details must be expressed economically.
7. Answers will vary; may include the throwing back of hands of the figure in the center, the expressions of sadness and shock on the faces of the women, their anxious leaning poses.

Part 2

8.–11. Because these activities will be based on individual opinion, answers will vary greatly, but should be shaped with skills learned in Chapters 2 through 5.

Study Guide 36 (Chapter 16, Section 1)

1. A period of great awakening, referring in art and history to the time of "rebirth and renewal" during the fourteenth and fifteenth centuries in Italy.
2. With huge wall paintings (frescoes) on the insides of their churches.
3. In northern Italy. It was the artistic capital during the Renaissance.
4. Figures were more lifelike. Architects imitated the ancient Roman buildings.
5. Neither serfs nor nobles, the middle class was the prosperous merchant, trader, or professional.
6. Middle-class people wanted to better themselves with education, and as they did, they began to be interested in the arts.
7. The continued tradition of creating large wall paintings in the churches and the development of linear perspective by the Italian artist Brunelleschi.
8. His use of both linear and aerial perspective, and his use of light and shadow.
9. Fresco.
10. Linear perspective: geometric principles, slanted lines, vanishing point. Aerial perspective: (atmosphere) hue, value, intensity.
11. A sculptor turned architect, he discovered and learned to use linear perspective.
12. Seeing a scene in a mirror reduces it to two dimensions, flattens the scene as it might appear on a canvas.
13. Linear perspective allows Masaccio to depict the buildings convincingly; aerial perspective suggests the endless space.
14. Some use of linear perspective, but no attempt to create deep space; figures are flat and exist in their own spaces.
15. Including an architectural setting that depended on linear perspective and placing figures in that setting.
16. The Baptistry doors in Florence.
17. Brunelleschi.
18. The lines of Ghiberti's design move around inside the frame, with figures overlapping in a normal way. Brunelleschi's design is in layers and is more static.
19. That the doors were fit to be the doors to Heaven. "The Gates of Paradise."

Study Guide 37 (Chapter 16, Section 2)

1. Giotto and Masaccio.
2. (a) Christ is solid form placed in center of picture.
   (b) His face framed by arch of hand, branch, and curve of the hill.
   (c) Vertical emphasis softened by curves in stream, branches, and horizon.
3. Use of sunlight.
4. When statues were to be viewed from below, figures had longer-than-normal upper bodies so they did not look distorted.
5. Contrapposto pose of figures, slight S curve to the body, gives them a very natural stance. Donatello's *St. George* is clothed and is to be viewed from below and from the front. Polyclitus's *Doryphoros* is not clothed and can be viewed from all sides.
6. He gave up sculpture for architecture, won another contest, and became very famous for building the dome of the Florence Cathedral.
7. Gothic ribs which met at the top of the dome were joined by horizontal sections outside the dome.
8. Sketch should show ribbed construction.
9. A balance of horizontal and vertical movement. Rounded curves and clean interior lines are used to create peaceful, dignified, and calm feelings.
10. The Medici family thought of him as a decorator who painted ornamental pictures.
11. The design qualities, the colors, the shape of the group, the formal balance (the W-shaped composition), all point to Formalism as the important aesthetic quality.
12. Diagram should consist of triangles and squares, all forming the W shape.
13. It could mean that Christianity was born out of the ruins of Paganism, or that Renaissance artists looked to the ancient classics for inspiration, or there may be other theories from students.
14. By having themselves painted into artworks in a pious pose.

Study Guide 38 (Chapter 16, Section 3)

1. Painting, sculpture, architecture, mathematics, botany, biology, poetry, music, hydraulics
2. He dissected cadavers to learn about the muscles, movement, and the mind.
3. He was a perfectionist, left things unfinished, experimented.
4. Judas is included in the painting; figures were all on the far side of the table, not grouped around the table.
5. *Ginevra de' Benci;* National Gallery of Art, Washington, D.C.
6. Thoughtful, serious, unhappy, pensive, and any others students may suggest.
7. *The Mona Lisa*
8. He was never satisfied with it.
9. A woman is holding a man's lifeless body in her lap. Her head is bowed and her eyes are closed.
10. The body of Mary is too large for the rest of the sculpture; may be in order not to make the body of Christ look too heavy for her to carry, focusing attention on the religious meaning.
11. The Pope kept changing his mind, put him on other projects, did not approve finished work on time.
12. He considered himself principally a sculptor; other famous artists had already painted the walls, and ceiling paintings are considered less important; the huge ceiling posed many difficulties.
13. The ceiling was divided into nine main sections, telling the Bible story of humanity from the creation to the flood.
14. Emotionalism.
15. Michelangelo struggled and led a lonely, difficult existence. Raphael was wealthy and socially successful during his career.
16. How to use shading for three-dimensional effect.
17. How to put energy and vitality in his figures.
18. Women were not generally expected to learn a trade or be educated outside the household. An artist's apprenticeship at the time was long and often required travel to art centers.

Study Guide 39 (Chapter 17, Section 1)

Part 1

1. The International style.
2. Religious symbolism; accurate, precise details.
3. Dry pigments were mixed with a binding agent and the paint applied to a surface prepared with a coating of gesso.
4. Artists had to work quickly, layers could not be transparent
5. Slower drying; artists could work more slowly and add more detail. Transparent glazes were possible, adding brilliance to the colors.
6. Jan van Eyck
7. Shoes removed—holy ground; dog—faithfulness; fruit—innocence; single burning candle—presence of God.
8. The richness and number of intricate details.
9. *The Ghent Altarpiece.* Central panel: angels, saints, and worshipers come toward a sacrificial lamb on an altar. The painting is filled with symbolism.
10. Imitationalism (realistic presentation of subject matter)

Part 2

11.–14. Charts should be completed in accordance with the operations described on pages 104 and 113. Judgments should be based on that material.

Study Guide 40 (Chapter 17, Section 2)

Part 1

1. More drama and emotion in depicting events; faces and gestures show emotion and response.
2. He preserved the Gothic tradition of good design and vivid emotion.
3. Answers may vary, but should include some of the following: van der Weyden created more emotion in his subject and used a closed space. Van Eyck included more traditional symbolism and created deep space.
4. Diagram calls for curves because the figures are not completely upright. The diagram should show the motion created by the curves and axis lines.
5. The panel creates a space at the top for the cross, and also forms an upside-down cross when taken as a whole.
6. The space between the two hands may be taken as the void between the living and the dead.
7. The wealth of the lady (jewelry, fine clothing), and her shy personality (clasped hands, downward glance).
8. The use of space: near figures appear smaller than some distant ones.
9. Precise detail from van Eyck; emotional content from van der Weyden.
10. The perspective is tilted; the stable floor is at an angle, pulling the viewer into the scene. Both kinds of perspective are used but figures are out of proportion.
11. He portrays them realistically, as common peasants, rather than idealizing them.

Part 2

12. The figures taken individually are realistic, but the distortion of the space rules out Imitationalism.
13. The elements of art are all important here: space (perspective), color, line, value, texture, and Formalism might be an option.
14. The pensive Mary, the prayerful Joseph, the surprised and awe-struck shepherds—all contribute to the emotional content in this work.
15. **(a)** shoes removed—holy ground
    (b) wheat—bread of the Eucharist
    (c) columbine and iris bouquet—the sorrows of Mary

Study Guide 41 (Chapter 18, Section 1)

1. Answers will vary. Venetian artists were influenced by the brilliant colors and carefully designed surfaces typical of the Byzantine style. Florentine artists painted realistic, if sometimes idealized, figures existing in real space, based on the more dramatic Greek and Roman models.

2. Landscapes.
3. Glowing effects, softened edges, rich colors
4. Details used: men's faces in shadow, ominous sky and soft light, figure in the background
5. Answers may vary. One example: Giorgione's figures show serenity. Titian's figures show agitation and energy.
6. Titian was influenced by Giorgione's use of landscape to set a mood and by Giorgione's use of oil paints to produce rich color and texture.
7. Answers will vary. *The Concert:* calm, gentle mood; soft lines; soft light. *The Entombment:* more dramatic mood; sharp edges, diagonals, intense contrast.
8. Michelangelo. Powerful figures, realism. The hand of Andrea Gritti is similar to the hand of Michelangelo's *Moses*.

Study Guide 42 (Chapter 18, Section 2)

Part 1

1. A setting of tension and disorder; the Protestant Reformation and the French invasion of Italy.
2. Answers will vary, but may include: imbalanced, exaggerated, dramatic, nervous, grotesque, vivid, elongated, graceful.
3. Parmigianino.
4. Three details: the "lifeless" form of the Christ child; the man in the far background; and the indoor-outdoor aspect of the background.
5. Answers may vary, but could include the dramatic, strange setting, the elongated figures, odd perspective, uneven light.
6. Highly emotional religious pictures, reminding people to follow the Church's teachings.
7. Titian: how to use contrasts of light and shadow; Tintoretto: how to add active movement to his compositions.
8. The Spanish king commissioned the painting but refused to hang it because it so displeased him. Velázquez had El Greco's work placed in the Escorial. Today it is regarded as one of El Greco's greatest works.
9. *The Burial of Count Orgaz.* Heavenly saints came to place the religious, devoted count in his tomb. The painting was meant to be a reminder of the villagers' eternal debt to the Church.
10. El Greco, himself, and his young son.

Part 2

11.–12. Answers will vary.

Study Guide 43 (Chapter 18, Section 3)

1. Gothic art: dreams, visions, the afterlife; Renaissance art: perspective, realistic portrayal, calm balance.
2. Grünewald's pictures were vivid, dramatic, exaggerated, powerful, dreamlike; Dürer created meticulously detailed pictures, with solid forms and lifelike shapes.
3. Grünewald's work is full of tension, conflict, high drama, agony. Raphael's is serene, placid, softly lined, and tranquil.
4. Answers will vary.
5. Dürer traveled from Germany to Italy to study. He applied the Renaissance style and ideas to his own work.
6. Dürer used traditional symbols from northern Gothic tradition. He also includes strange creatures. Dürer treats the horse and rider in the Renaissance style, creating solid, realistic forms. He also creates depth by overlapping figures.
7. The dog—loyalty; the horse and knight—calmness, steadfastness; the strange figures—death and the devil; Jerusalem—heavenly destination.
8. Dürer accepted Luther's principles that were in conflict with the Roman church. He was involved with the Reformation.
9. Perspective; theory of proportions.
10. Bosch's paintings portray stories of good and evil, reflecting the religious conflicts of the time.
11. The dying man looks at the crucifix window while holding his hand out for money. An earlier scene is included at the bottom of the painting that shows another instance of

indecision. (Bosch often pictured the devil as a fool or clown.)

12. Bruegel based his pictures on good and evil, reflecting the unsettled times in sixteenth-century Netherlands.
13. Clear, concise detail; strong emphasis on symbolism rather than realistic perspective and round, solid figures.
14. The principle axis line runs downward from the upper left to the lower right. The downward motion emphasizes a descending fall.
15. Hans Holbein; lifelike portraits.
16. It was a painting given as a gift of King Henry's long-awaited son. Unfortunately, the son, portrayed in royal garments, was a short-lived king who died at the age of sixteen.
17. King Henry VIII sent Holbein to paint a portrait of his future queen. Holbein painted a flattering portrait of Anne, which persuaded the king to marry her.

Study Guide 44 (Chapter 19, Section 1)

Part 1

1. An effort by the Catholic church to regain the power it had lost during the Reformation; in Rome, Italy.
2. Goals: to restore religious spirit, make Rome the most beautiful city in the world, and lure people back to the Church.
3. A new style developed in church architecture: sculpted scrolls on the façade, more sculptural qualities, an overall effect of movement.
4. Il Gesù: scroll work, statues in niches. San Carlo alle Quattro Fontane: columns, sculpted façade, niches, convex and concave surfaces.
5. Elaborate drapery, light and shadow, modeling, deep undercutting for contrasts, movement, drama.
6. The effect of extending far into the heavens. The viewer does not know where the architecture of the building leaves off and the painting begins.
7. Emotionalism, expressive qualities.
8. Motion, strong contrasts of light and dark.
9. The horse, figure on the ground, and man holding the horse are all in motion. The light is exaggerated and dramatic.
10. She was the first woman artist in the history of Western art to have impact on the art of her time. She helped spread Caravaggio's style throughout Italy.
11. Titian—color; Tintoretto—dramatic composition; Michelangelo—twisting, powerful figures; Caravaggio—use of light; northern painters like van Eyck—realistic detail.

Part 2

12. Design charts will vary.
13. Answers may vary. For example, color, gradation: the light and shadow on the figures.
14. Answers may include: dramatic light on Daniel; realistic portrayal of lions; Daniel in an active, dramatic pose; contrasts between light and shadow; emotional mood.

Study Guide 45 (Chapter 19, Section 2)

1. Because the Dutch Protestants did not want religious sculptures or paintings in their churches.
2. Paintings of people in everyday life, engaged in everyday activities.
3. Because the market from ordinary citizens was growing, and artists could make a living by specializing in particular areas: portraits, still life, seascapes.
4. Portraits that were "photographic," people with realistic, fleeting expressions.
5. His use of light for dramatic effect.
6. Answers will vary, but should include: the artist is across the room studying the art on the easel and is not as important as the easel; the painting on the easel is not visible, but is dramatically lit from an unseen source; the mood is subdued.
7. Steen and Vermeer.
8. Skill in creating light, shadow, and atmosphere; compositions that bring the viewer into the picture; stories of common people and familiar events.

9. The varying poses and actions of the figures in the painting; some laughing, some crying, some communicating with one another; the scattered toys, the half-eaten food.
10. (Diagram) Answers may vary. Use of light, rounded solid figures, detail, emotional content, motion.
11. Use of diagonal lines to lead to the important parts, overlapped figures, darkening the background.
12. Theatrical effect due to dramatic lighting.

Study Guide 46 (Chapter 19, Section 3)

1. The Spanish painted religious subjects. The Dutch painted everyday scenes.
2. Ribera moved to Rome and studied art there. He utilized Caravaggio's strong dramatic lighting and realism.
3. Both used drama and lighting effects. However, Rubens liked massive pictures full of people; Ribera's were more spare, with just a few figures.
4. The expressions of the faces on the left, as opposed to those on the right; the smoke on the left indicating something burning; the erect lances on the right as opposed to the left.
5. The mirror, the open door, linear and aerial perspective.
6. Murillo was an orphan and a commoner; Velázquez was from a noble family. Velázquez's painting is a royal portrait; Murillo's painting is of common people.
7. Diagram should show the motion of all the figures in the painting.
8. All the motion leads the viewer toward the center of the picture and the two central figures.
9. Artists could not depend on a universal church for support and had to seek other means of pursuing their art. They were more free to paint nonreligious subjects, but they had to be more resourceful.

Study Guide 47 (Chapter 20, Section 1)

1. Louis XIV, "The Sun King."
2. *Rocaille,* the French word meaning pebble or rockwork (used to decorate artificial grottos) became the label for ornamental, detailed decorative art called Rococo.
3. Baroque art was heavily dramatic; Rococo art was more carefree. Baroque vivid contrasts of light and shadow and strong color gave way to Rococo soft contrasts and pastel colors.
4. Literal: figures dressed in high fashion move with graceful ease; the statue of Venus is covered with flowers; group of aristocrats. Design: silvery colors, circular patterns of smooth-flowing lines in the composition. These qualities contribute to the *expressive* qualities of a dreamlike atmosphere, feeling of a happy, carefree scene. (Answers may vary slightly.)
5. The lower part of the composition is united by the contour lines and the axis lines formed by the ropes, telescope, and water. The landscape and sky are tied together by the repetition of the rounded contours in the clouds and trees.
6. Answers may vary. Similarities: subjects—small aristocratic figures in landscape setting with vast sky and clouds; highly decorative. Differences: Watteau—more dreamlike atmosphere, Fragonard—more realistic.
7. Curved forms; elaborate ornamentation.
8. By painting them in arrangements that gave them dignity and worth through his use of color, light, and texture.
9. Design charts will vary.
10. Answers will vary somewhat, but may include: value (non-color); the gradation of values described in the text. Shape: balance with the off-center figure balanced by the table; variety with the figure that is making a motion, and the still life of the table; emphasis with the focus of attention in the work area, the hands, towel, table, and so on.
11. The use of light and shadow, detail, and the subject of an everyday scene.

Study Guide 48 (Chapter 20, Section 2)

Part 1

1. The wealthy aristocracy and the Stuart royal family. Portrait painting became popular.
2. His ability to paint fine portraits, especially of children. He painted what the English nobility desired.
3. The two were rivals; Reynolds said cool colors like blue should be used only in the background; Gainsborough painted *The Blue Boy* in response.
4. Answers will vary.
5. Gainsborough and Reynolds painted aristocracy, in idealized surroundings; Hogarth painted all sorts of people in everyday situations in a witty, sometimes unflattering or satirical way.
6. *The Marriage Contract*. Hogarth satirizes the custom of arranged marriages. Tone and purpose are revealed in the gestures, poses, and expressions of the figures.
7. The great fire of London in 1666 destroyed most of the city, including eighty-nine churches.
8. Wren designed and built many of the buildings after the London fire, including fifty-one parish churches and St. Paul's Cathedral. He also personally supervised the construction of each. He designed churches suited for their settings with steeples so they would be seen among other buildings.
9. St. Paul's: façade—light and dark values; porches at two levels supported by huge columns; tympanum and dome; two towers; overall unity.

Part 2

10. (a) *The Duchess of Alba;* portrait of an aristocrat; formal setting, unemotional, standing pose
    (b) *The Third of May, 1808;* an execution scene; asymmetrical, dramatic, protest against killing and war
    (c) *The Giant;* a giant looking up over his shoulder; an imagined giant seated at edge of a landscape.

11.–12. Answers will vary.

13. Goya went through transitions as an artist from being a society painter to expressing protest against war to painting from imagination. By painting subjects from his own visions and dreams, Goya established a new direction for art.

Study Guide 48a (Chapter 21, Section 1)

1. Origins: art exhibits, organized by the Academies. Importance: as social events and opportunities for artists to display their work.
2. Interest was renewed by the discovery of Pompeii and Herculaneum in the 1730s and 1740s. The French Revolution's spirit of freedom was thought to be best illustrated by Greek and Roman artwork, as in David's work.
3. David's skillful, classical portrayal of Marat as a calm, innocent person ignored Marat's support of violence. The painting was meant to arouse outrage at the murder of Marat.
4. To be flattered, portrayed with large, expressive eyes.
5. He won the *Prix de Rome* and was the best-known student of Jacques Louis David, and returned to Paris when the Neoclassic movement was without a leader.
6. Idealized pose, lack of emotionalism, sculpted contours
7. Line and smooth contours.
8. Aesthetic sense, beauty, humility, nobility.

Study Guide 49 (Chapter 21, Section 2)

Part 1

1. Romanticism stresses drama and emotion. Neoclassicism stresses nobility of subject matter and balance.
2. Dramatic light and shadow; portrayal of a scene with drama and action; powerful figures; diagonal composition; broad range of emotions.
3. Baroque, because of the powerful figures, the emphasis on emotion.

4. His travels to Africa; his study of the works of Constable.
5. They were rivals for the prizes awarded by the Academy. They held different views of art.
6. Design charts will vary.
7. Color.
8. Bright greens and reds in the costumes of the hunters; vivid colors side by side in sky and landscape.

Part 2

9. Constable painted full landscape scenes as the eye actually sees them and with great detail.
10. Turner focused on light and atmosphere and was not so interested in realistic detail.
11. Critics failed to understand Turner's artistic goals. His work was judged on concepts of Realism.
12. Charts and responses will vary.
13. Answers will vary but should include reasons to support preferences.
14. Growth of the working class due to the industrial revolution.
15. Courbet painted common people attending a funeral as an ordinary event without religious meaning.
16. Imitationalism; showing an event as it actually occurred.
17. Courbet painted very realistically with careful brushstrokes; Manet used a variety of brushstrokes that resulted in a richly textured surface.
18. **a.** Asymmetrical
    b. Use of paint strokes; variety of lines, curved for figures and straight for fence.
    c. Girl's arm extends across space to the woman, unifying the figures.
19. Animals.
20. Romanticism—movement and drama in the action.

    Realism—correct anatomy and proportion of horses.

Study Guide 50 (Chapter 21, Section 3)

1. To catch the flickering quality of sunlight; to capture the fleeting moment, the impression of reality.
2. They painted outdoors; used quick, short brushstrokes.
3. From the Monet picture: *Impression: Sunrise.*
4. They thought the painting looked hastily done, unfinished.
5. To capture the subject in the changing light. He painted different versions to capture the changing colors as the sunlight changed.
6. The dabs of color simulate flickering sunlight; the use of side-by-side complementary colors produces a shimmering effect.
7. Japanese prints, photographs.
8. Elegant patterns of lines, delicate colors, showing the world in new ways, entire figures not always shown, flat shapes.
9. Unposed views of people were shown, as in candid snapshots.
10. The figure of the man goes off the page; unusual view across the tables; genre scene; delicate, flat colors.
11. The unposed look of the figures; out-of-focus items closest to viewer.
12. His interest in drawing; line, form, movement of anatomy.
13. Horses, ballet dancers.
14. She was introduced to Impressionism by Degas.
15. Attention is drawn to the subject's face by the encircling, leading axis lines of the arms and folds of the nightgown.
16. Degas turned to sculpture; Cassatt to advising purchasers of fine art.
17. She posed her subjects for short times and then painted them from memory.
18. He portrayed fleeting moments, sculpted so that light and shadow would interplay on the uneven surface.

Study Guide 51 (Chapter 22, Section 1)

Part 1

1. Structure, form; not only the Impressionistic, momentary effects of sunlight.
2. Cézanne, van Gogh, Gauguin.
3. Faithful reproduction of nature.
4. Cézanne started with nature but did not feel bound to it. He was more interested in construction than representation.
5. He placed patches of color side by side to form planes; created a three-dimensional effect with warm and cool colors.
6. He could study them closely for long periods of time, and he could position still-life objects to create a unified design.
7. Answers may vary. Solid, massive quality; volume.
8. Answers will vary but should include emphasis on depth and perspective in the Chardin work, flat planes in the painting by Cézanne; more faithful reproduction of reality in the Chardin, interest in mass, solid qualities of forms in Cézanne's.

9.–10. Answers will vary.

Part 2

11. Answers will vary but should include the use of strong parallel brushstrokes; joining of strokes of different colors, for effect. Comparison should note Cézanne's blocks of smooth color contrasted with van Gogh's slashes of color.
12. Answers will vary but may refer to the dark, somber mood, lack of variation in color, the dim light over the table, the silence implied by the noncommunicating figures, and one figure with her back turned. The element of color (drab).
13. The use of large, flat areas of color and strange tilting of perspective, both present in *The Bedroom at Arles.*

14.–15. Answers will vary.

Part 3

16. He left his well-paying job and his family, as he traveled widely to find the place and people he wanted to paint.
17. Tahiti, in the South Seas.
18. Charts will vary.
19. Answers will vary. Most of the forms are flat planes of color, overlapping with curving lines.
20. They both believed an artist does not need to copy nature but can exaggerate or alter what is seen and paint from his or her own imagination and ideas.

Study Guide 52 (Chapter 22, Section 2)

Part 1

1. Both artists were Realists, showed attention to detail, painted everyday scenes in American life.
2. Army life; everyday life, such as schoolrooms, seascapes, fishing scenes, nature.
3. Courbet, Velázquez, Hals, Rembrandt, and a Neoclassic teacher/artist in Paris.
4. Homer: works were too sketchy, looked unfinished. Eakins: his paintings were too real and critics objected to things like the blood on the scalpel and hands in the painting. Answers will vary.
5. Student's choice. Any choice is acceptable as long as the reason is understood.
6. Ryder's work was fanciful, less realistic; his life more unconventional and antisocial.
7. A nineteenth-century black portrait artist who had his works attributed to others and is now being given recognition for his work.
8. First prize, Philadelphia Centennial Exhibition for his painting *Under the Oaks.*
9. Thomas Eakins.
10. He was not successful in America. He followed the route of other artists.

Part 2

11.–15. Answers will vary.

Study Guide 53 (Chapter 23, Section 1)

Part 1

1. Matisse.
2. Free, wild, brightly colored, simple in design.
3. An art critic who did not approve of the style coined the name that means "wild beasts."
4. **(a)** extended his use of color
   (b) extended his use of flat, broad shapes, and lively line patterns.
5. Strips away the unnecessary details, unifies the painting, suspends the objects in the studio in midair to be examined.
6. By using linear perspective.
7. Line, space (others may be valid).
8. To bring pleasure and peaceful viewing to the person looking at the painting.
9. With the red color field
10. He reduced his designs to paper cutouts that he then arranged into compositions.
11. To bring pleasure to the viewer.
12. Rouault's work shows the more sorrowful side of life, as opposed to the work of Matisse, which was created to be joyful and peaceful. Rouault's works are darker, denser, and more disturbing. However, both viewed art as a form of personal expression—to present their own thoughts and feelings about the world.
13. To emphasize the downward lines on the face of the king; to create the effect of stained glass; to create unity in the picture.

Part 2

14. An era of phony elegance with tensions that finally resulted in the First World War.
15. His art revealed tension, hardships, and was a commentary on the times. When his work was disapproved of by Hitler, Kirchner took his own life in a fit of depression.
16. Lithographs, etchings, woodcuts, to reach the greatest number of viewers.
17. The Fauves: van Gogh, Munch, and other German Expressionists.
18. The death of his sister affected him deeply and is probably the subject of the painting *The Sick Child.* He chose to describe inner feelings.
19. Answers will vary.
20. He freed the artist from subject matter.
21. Charts will vary.
22. Emotionalism is the best answer, because Kandinsky's main goal was to express feelings.

Part 3

23. Cézanne.
24. **(a)** Lines may end unexpectedly or continue when you expect them to end.
    (b) Space is manipulated by confusing which part of a shape is in front or in back of another.
    (c) Complex arrangement, breaking up, and overlapping of shapes.
    (d) Colors associated with objects are not used; drab colors are substituted.
25. Cubists, wanting to make their artworks richer, added a variety of textures, string, labels, and other materials.
26. Intellectual. Shapes and figures were manipulated deliberately, not as an emotional expression.
27. The exaggeration of Expressionism can be seen in the distortions, expressions, and positions of the human figures. Cubism is used in the elements that are viewed from more than one angle at once, e.g., the cow on the upper-left corner or the man's face in the lower-left corner.
28. Picasso constantly changed styles; Braque maintained that a painting is a flat surface and remained committed to that idea.
29. Both artists convey a gentle, comfortable feeling in their work, echoing the classical characteristics of balance and peacefulness.
30. The triangles of body, arm, leg.

Study Guide 54 (Chapter 23, Section 2)

1. The wall painting of medieval and later times, to teach a message, illustrate a religious story.
2. Revolutions, political beliefs, native traditions, festivals, and legends.

3. To take their art out of the museum and make it visible to many more people.
4. Diego Rivera: paintings of peasants in round, sturdy figures; bright colors. José Clemente Orozco: strong, emotional style. David Alfaro Siqueiros: three-dimensional style, emotional content.
5. Changes were taking place that took artists out of a conservative slumber.
6. First, the staring cat on the fence, then the direction of the moving cat, the direction of the arm, across the clothesline and fenceline to the face at the window, and back to the cat.
7. Sports. He captured the movement of athletes in his paintings.
8. They rebelled against academic idealism and painted life around them, such as cafes, streets, alleys, theaters.
9. Charts will vary.
10. Emotionalism, although other answers may also be acceptable.
11. Realism in the Bellows, however stylized, is completely different than the lack of subject matter in the Kandinsky.
12. The strong vertical and angular lines.
13. An art show held in a New York armory in 1913, which was created to show modern works of European as well as American artists.
14. Europeans had seen modern styles develop, whereas most Americans had not, and reacted with laughter, anger, and attempts to understand.
15. Many Americans turned away from the conservative style and began to experiment with new styles.

Study Guide 55 (Chapter 23, Section 3)

1. New industrial methods and materials.
2. Materials: iron, steel, exposed ironwork with open beams of small angle irons and flat irons. Construction: prefabricated pieces, riveted together (by 150 men in seventeen months).
3. To imitate the designs of nature.
4. Answers will vary, may include: whimsical, enchanted, childlike, fanciful, softly contoured.
5. The Hearst Estate, at San Simeon.
6. She did not publicize herself, letting her work speak for itself.
7. Louis Sullivan.
8. Answers will vary but should mention the conservative style, classic lines, steel-beam support, vertical pillars of brick, decorative elements.
9. Simple, square lines; a steel cage or frame as the support for the structure; glass and concrete.

Study Guide 56 (Chapter 24, Section 1)

1. Art that ridiculed contemporary culture and traditional art forms. Disillusionment, anxiety, lack of prosperity, and unrest in the years that followed World War I.
2. The painting portrays the artist's inner world of dreams, fantasy, and the subconscious rather than real objects or subjects.
3. Miró: childlike, playful forms, usually unrecognizable. Dali: real images, but twisted and often strange and grotesque.
4. Answers will vary. Klee combined his imagination with his observations of the wonders around him: movement of fish, butterflies, characteristics of shells, coral, and stained glass. The Surrealists focused more on the inner world of the subconscious, even though they may have painted real objects.
5. Kay Sage's *No Passing:* repeated architectural forms seem to stand on a strange, deserted planet.
6. Regionalism: art of scenes and events that could be understood in a clear, simple way. Surrealism: more symbolic images, mysterious.
7. Answers may vary. *American Gothic,* Wood: expressions of the couple, their stance; simple faith, determination. *Drugstore,* Hopper: lights viewed through windows on dark, deserted streets; loneliness of urban life.

8. **(a)** Stuart Davis: urban America; interwoven colors, shapes, and textures.
   (b) Georgia O'Keeffe: nature; close-up views.
   (c) Alice Neel: unique portraits, elements of exaggeration.
   (d) Jacob Lawrence: urban scenes; simplified, flat, and colorful shapes to tell a story.
9. No realistic subject matter; shows feelings and emotions; emphasis on physical action of painting; spontaneous, often random brushstrokes; spilled, spattered, dribbled applications of paint to canvas.
10. **(a)** Motherwell; *Elegy to the Spanish Republic 108;* huge, black shapes before a background of delicate, warm hues.
    (b) Pollock; *Cathedral;* expression of feeling through the physical act of painting, unplanned.
    (c) Frankenthaler; *Interior Landscape;* thinned paint poured on unprimed canvas, flowing, graceful, free-form shapes.
    (d) de Kooning; *Woman VI;* incomplete image, sweeping, violent brushstrokes, rich color.

Study Guide 57 (Chapter 24, Section 2)

Part 1

1. Answers may vary. Sculptors broke away from realism; studied their materials as a guide to finding new forms. Moore: worked without a model, studied the stone from different angles. Hepworth: studied nature and natural materials.
2. Free forms, hollowed-out spaces, suggested movement, smooth lines.
3. The same geometric shapes are found in the paintings of Braque and Picasso but now in three-dimensional form. Flat surfaces were placed at various angles.
4. Texture. Contrasts between skin, shawls, skirts. Blocks of textures create shapes.
5. A hanging sculpture that moves: it is a constantly changing design, depending on how the parts are interacting at any given moment. *Pomegranate* description: answers may vary.
6. She combined a number of materials: wood, metal, found objects, to create an assemblage, visually unified by one color of paint.
7. Nevelson: nonobjective forms, assemblage of found objects, often painted one color; a three-dimensional collage. Hanson: very realistic portraits of people made from fiberglass, hair, and clothes.

Part 2

8. Notre Dame du Haut is free-form and unconventional, with walls that bend and curve, windows that cut through thick walls, a billowing roof.
9. **(a)** Guggenheim Museum, New York City, circular design with spiral galleries.
   (b) East Building of the National Gallery of Art, Washington, D.C., two triangular buildings to fit in the space where two streets meet.
10. **(a)** Use of abstract, nonconventional forms to create architectural designs.
    (b) Focus on the use of a building to determine the design.
    (c) Best use of available space, sculptural outside as well as inside.
11. Answers may vary. A wall is made up of 1,560 panels with the names of American servicemen and servicewomen lost or missing. To read the names, viewers must descend into the earth and gradually work their way upward.
12. Answers will vary. For example: Notre Dame du Haut (Le Corbusier); *Reclining Figure* (Moore)
    (a) shape/form: both have rounded, bending forms
    (b) space: Moore's cut openings and Le Corbusier's windows create a sense of movement around and through the solid structures.
    (c) value: The contours of each work contribute to the contrast of lights and shadows that become part of the structures.

Part 3

13. Pop, Op, Hard-edge, and Photo-Realism
14. They used pictures of familiar household (manufactured) objects, to suggest that the mass media were shaping people's lives.
15. Oldenburg: too much reliance on commercial/industrial products. Lindner: dominance of rock music penetrating the performer. Answers may vary.
16. A nonobjective art movement; to create an impression of movement, optical illusion. United States, Germany, Italy.
17. Riley: gradual changes of color, wavy lines to add movement. Agam: multiple images created by combining and superimposing designs.
18. Smooth surfaces, hard edges, pure colors, geometric shapes, great precision.
19. A realistic style that looked photographic; 1970s.
20. Answers may include reference to the expressive quality of the works by both artists; the dramatic use of light and shadows to create an effect.
21. **(a)** objects: calendar, watch, egg timer, and/or burning candle.

    (b) selection: symbols of time, temporality. Answers may vary.
22. He captures the essence of reality, rather than presenting a photographic copy of his subjects.
23. Answers may vary, but should refer to the autobiographical information in the chapter. Wyeth's father was killed in an automobile-train accident in 1945 on the other side of the hill that appears in this and other paintings. Wyeth learned to paint with his father and had been very close to him. The boy in the painting is alone.
24. Landscape painters working in Toronto, Canada, around 1920. They developed a unique style of modern art.
25. Love of nature, focusing on the details of natural forms as subject.